C000243296

ABOUT THIS BOOK

SUBJECT MATTER

This book is an introduction to the construction and syntax of English sentences. It assumes a knowledge of basic grammar, and in particular of the parts of speech, — as covered in Book One of the Series, 'Words'.

In addition to its primary purpose of teaching grammar and syntax, this book is also designed to help in the development of vocabulary and spelling, comprehension skills and essay writing; and to give an insight into the workings of many foreign languages. A great deal of information has deliberately been included, in a precise but readable manner, and using formal terminology where possible.

This book will provide the children using it with a knowledge of the structure of their own language. Knowledge is power, and understanding *how* the language works will give those children the ability to use English for themselves far more effectively.

LAYOUT

The format is that of a (re-usable) workbook. Each double page provides a factsheet on a particular topic facing a worksheet designed both to test the knowledge provided and to help the child in its use. Putting the two together makes reference back very simple. Testsheets to monitor progress are provided at the end of the book, together with an index and glossary.

USE

The factsheets can be used directly by the child as an information source. Alternatively they can be used to provide the basis of the teaching content of a lesson, or as reinforcement to the teacher's own lesson plans and scheme of work.

The worksheets are intended to be used by children working alone or in groups, with support and assistance available from the teacher (or from parents).

This book can be readily used for work done at home.

A suggested marking scheme is provided for each exercise and worksheet with a total of 1,500 marks for all 20, plus another 500 for the testsheets. Teachers may of course wish to vary the weightings given to individual exercises, or to employ their own marking schemes.

However, it is envisaged that the marking of the worksheets *with* the children who have done them will in itself provide a useful teaching vehicle.

AGE/ABILITY RANGE

The content of this book has been intensively tested with pupils as young as nine and as old as 15, with a remarkable degree of success.

More or less support will of course be required from the teacher depending on the age and ability of the children using the book.

The book is best suited to top primary and lower secondary school pupils, or pupils in middle and preparatory schools, in the age range 10+ to 14+ and of average or above average ability. It is intended as the second part of a course, and is therefore best used in conjunction with Book One. However, it can be used by any pupils who have received an initial grounding in grammar. It can also be used as a revision primer for older pupils.

A reading age of 11+ is recommended, and the book would not generally be suitable for use with remedial teaching groups.

FACTSHEET ONE

THE SUBJECT OF THE VERB

Nearly all sentences in English contain a verb.

The verb is the 'doing word'; it tells you the action that is happening.

Two points to note, however:— A verb is a doing word, not the name of an action; the word *action* is a noun, the word *act*, in 'He acts the part well' for example, is a verb.

Secondly, not all sentences must have a verb. 'When?'; 'Forward, soldiers of the Imperial Guard!'; 'Oh dear!' are all sentences of a sort, yet they do not have verbs.

The parts of a verb which are used in sentences to express an action are called FINITE VERBS.

Nouns and adjectives formed from the parts of a verb are NOT finite verbs.

Remember that a verb may be in more than one piece: He *is being chased*; I *should have been going*. Here the words in italics are all part of the verb.

A finite verb, the verb expressing the action in the sentence, requires a SUBJECT.

The SUBJECT is the person, animal or thing which is performing the action.

If a verb is a doing word, then the subject is the 'do-er'.

Since an action has to be performed by someone or something, as you might expect the subject of the verb, the someone or something, has to be a NOUN, a PRONOUN, or a group of words performing the function of a noun.

As you know, a noun is a naming word, — a person, place, creature, or thing.

A pronoun is a word standing in place of a noun. (We need pronouns because it is obviously inconvenient to say 'This person here' every time we mean 'I'.)

The personal pronouns which are used as the subjects of verbs are as follows:—

I YOU HE SHE IT WE THEY

The following personal pronouns are *never* the subjects of Verbs:—

ME HIM HER US THEM

There are other pronouns which can be verb subjects:- This, That, These, Those (Demonstrative pronouns).

Who, Which, What, That (Relative and interrogative pronouns).

Look at this verb written out in the present tense, showing all the *persons* with their personal pronouns:—

I WRITE	(First person singular)	WE WRITE	(First person plural)
YOU WRITE	(Second person singular)	YOU WRITE	(Second person plural: notice that 'you' may be singular or plural)
HE WRITES	(Third person singular)		
SHE WRITES	(also Third person singular)	THEY WRITE	(Third person plural).
IT WRITES	(also Third person singular)		

When a NOUN is the SUBJECT it is always THIRD PERSON. It is third person singular, when the noun is singular; if the noun is plural, then the subject is obviously third person plural.

Thus:- 'The woman writes': subject 'woman', — singular (there is only one woman), therefore third person singular; but 'The women write': subject 'women', — plural (there is more than one woman), therefore third person plural.

(a) Write out the following sentences, and at the end of each write the *finite* verb (or verbs — there may be more then one). Remember that a single verb may consist of several words, and you must include all of them when you write down the verb.

(1) Actions speak louder than words.

(2) Round and round the rugged rocks the ragged rascal ran.

(3) To die is but for suffering to cease.

(4) We would all benefit from working harder.

(5) I have never liked gardening, especially mowing the lawn.

(6) Your writing reminds me of the tracks of a small and very inky octopus, Benjamin.

(7) Mrs Chubb should have been interviewed by the appointments board today.

(8) And did those feet, in ancient times, walk upon England's mountains green?

(9) Charge for the guns, my lads, and the devil take the hindmost. (TWO)

(10)

(b) Write out the following sentences, and at the end of each write the *subject* of the verb. Remember that the subject may well consist of more than one word.

(1) I cannot abide that Mavis Thompson.

(2) Have you seen my glasses anywhere?

(3) Where on earth has Emma got to now?

(4) Jack and Jill went up the hill.

(5) The washing machine has broken down again.

(6) Who is responsible for this mess?

(7) That is not the way to make toffee.

(8) Your singing reminds me of the water going down the plug-hole, Benedict.

(9) To delay any longer is to lay ourselves open to enormous risks.

(10) Out of the hitherto unbroken silence, a whispering, echoing, yet almost inaudible sigh flitted across the darkened spaces of the room.

(20)

(c) Write out these sentences, inserting the correct form of the subject or verb from the choices that are given to you in the brackets. Underline your answer.

(1) The (baby/babies) is crying again.

(2) The (child/children) were playing in the street.

(3) What shall (we/you) do with the drunken sailor?

(4) Who (was/were) you with last night?

(5) Ellen and I (are/am/is) going to the shops.

(6) They asked us if (us/we) could come to the pictures.

(7) Fighting for our rights (have/has) only brought us further wrongs.

(8) (Him and me/He and I/Him and I) (was/were) not interested in the offer. (TWO)

(9) To re-arrange the furniture and replace the aspidistra in its pot (was/ were) the work of a moment.

(10)

(d) Insert a verb IN THE PRESENT TENSE in the spaces shown, so that when you have inserted all the verbs the story makes good sense:—

The hideous form of the spectre ……… from out of the cellar. Mike ………, though his sister, Meg, ……… silent. They both ……… in horrified fascination at the thing before them, as slowly, with fluttering movements, it ……… them, coming ever nearer. The light of the torch ……… fainter, and the candles suddenly ……… out, all at once. It ……… an accusing finger at them.

"Do you think haunted houses run themselves for nothing? Where ……… your admission fees?" ……… the unearthly voice.

(20)

FACTSHEET TWO

AGREEMENT (1)

Look back at the verb written out in the present tense on the previous Factsheet. You will see that it could not be more straightforward, — except in the case of the THIRD PERSON SINGULAR. This has three forms, *he, she,* and *it,* among the personal pronouns. It is also the person of the verb that is used when any singular noun is the subject. This tends to make it the most commonly used person of the verb, and it is important to give it the '-S' ending.

But there are other variations in the form of the verb, found in other tenses, which occur depending on the subject.

Firstly there is the special case of the verb TO BE:—

I <u>AM</u> and he or she or it <u>IS</u>; but we, you or they <u>ARE.</u>

I <u>WAS,</u> and he, she or it <u>WAS</u>; but we, you or they <u>WERE.</u>

These variations are important because the verb TO BE is used to form the continuous present tense ('I am writing' etc.) and the imperfect tense ('I was writing' etc.)

Then we have the other auxiliary verb which changes its form; TO HAVE:—

I, you, we and they <u>HAVE</u>; but he, she or it <u>HAS.</u>

You need to remember this every time you use a perfect tense ('I have written' etc.)

There is also the future tense, where we have:—

I <u>SHALL</u> and we <u>SHALL</u>; but you <u>WILL</u>, he <u>WILL</u>, it <u>WILL</u> and they <u>WILL.</u> ('I shall write' etc.)

It is now very common to find 'I will' and 'we will' instead of 'I shall' and 'we shall'. Strictly speaking 'I will' gives an additional idea of purpose or intention, not just future time. Similarly 'you shall', 'he shall' etc. suggest something like a command. In your writing try to use 'shall' for the first person (singular and plural) of the future tense — unless you want to give the idea of intention or purpose.

In the subjunctive/conditional 'would' tends to imply possibility, doubt — or a condition; 'should' gives an idea of obligation, or 'having to'.

All this is generally summed up in the rule: A VERB MUST AGREE WITH ITS SUBJECT. This means, in effect, that you must make sure you have not put the incorrect form of the verb with a particular subject. For example, you do not write any of the following:—

I is writing, he am going; they was naughty; you talks a lot; she were very pretty; we will go now; they has done it.

The same applies when it is a noun subject. If the noun is singular, make sure you use the singular form of the third person. If you are using a tense where there is no change, much of the time there is no difficulty, as for example in 'The tiger snarled' and 'The tigers snarled' — past tense. They are in the past tense which does not change at all for any of the persons. In the present tense though, you need to write 'The tiger snarl<u>s</u>' (singular), but 'The tiger<u>s</u> snarl' (plural); or 'The tiger <u>is</u> snarling' (singular), but 'The tiger<u>s</u> <u>are</u> snarling' (plural). In the imperfect tense you would have: 'The tiger <u>was</u> snarling' and 'The tiger<u>s</u> <u>were</u> snarling'; and in the perfect: 'The tiger <u>has</u> snarled' and 'The tiger<u>s</u> <u>have</u> snarled'.

There is another important point to bear in mind about changing the ending of the verb in the third person singular — spelling! Look at the following examples:—

Verbs ending in -Y, change Y to I and add -ES (*Fly — flies, defy — defies, try — tries*). (Note that this does not apply to verbs ending in -EY, -AY, -OY and -UY; *I play, he plays etc.*)

Verbs ending in -S, -SH, -CH, and -X add -ES (*Box — boxes; thrash — thrashes; scratch — scratches.*)

Verbs ending in -O also add -ES (There are not many of these, but they include *Do — Does,* and *Go — Goes*).

WORSHEET TWO

(a) Insert the correct form of the auxiliary verb from the choices given you:—

   (1) I (am/were) going to town today.

   (2) I (am/was) going to town yesterday.

   (3) I (will/shall) be going to town tommorrow.

   (4) (Are/Is) all of you coming with me?

   (5) (Was/Were) it those boys from next door again?

   (6) They (were/was) climbing on our fence yesterday.

   (7) (Have/Has) their father no control over them?

   (8) The writings of the professor on the precise construction of his antigravity machine (is/are) rather obscure.

   (9) If the destruction of an entire row of houses (is/are) to be avoided, it (will/shall) be necessary to re-route the proposed by-pass.

   (TWO)

   (10)

(b) In this exercise, *some* of the verbs have been written incorrectly. Write out all the sentences, and correct any errors you find. Underline the words you have changed.

   (1) The tiger, deep in the forests, were snarling throughout the long night.

   (2) How many tigers have the men from the zoo captured this week?

   (3) The trap we have dug catchs them quite easily, but getting them out of the pit present us with real problems.

   (4) Emily plaies so nicely with that robot .....

   (5) Where was they going, I wondered.

   (6) He dose not like chips, but he shall eat boiled potatoes if I cooks them lightly.

   (7) However much he trys, Lewis shall never be as clever as his sisters.

   (You should have made TEN corrections).

   (10)

(c) Rewrite these sentences, changing both the VERB and SUBJECT from singular to plural. Do not change any other words, unless you have to in order to ensure that the sentence continues to make sense; there are several changes of this sort necessary.

   (1) The cat is chasing the mice.

   (2) Does she take sugar?

   (3) That boy always tries to create a disturbance in my class.

   (4) You should never have eaten that third helping of pudding.

   (5) I have never been so surprised in my life.

   (6) It was going to be a long speech.

   (7) She is waiting for a letter from her mother, but waiting, I am afraid, in vain.

   (You should have made TWENTY changes).

   (20)

(d) In this exercise the subjects and verbs are in the plural, and your job is to change them into the singular. Once again do not make any other changes, unless they are necessary to preserve the sense, — and once again there are several such changes necessary.

   (1) They fly through the air with the greatest of ease.

   (2) We were sitting quietly in the front room sipping our tea.

   (3) Their teachers have never been pleased with those boys' work.

   (4) The girls watch and wait in complete silence while the boys leave their hut; then they rush in and lock the door behind them with a squeal of glee.

   (Again, you should have made TWENTY changes).

   (20)

FACTSHEET THREE

AGREEMENT (2)

There are some complications involved in making the verb agree with its subject.

Collective nouns in the singular take a singular verb, even though they refer to several people, animals or things:—

'A herd of cattle *was* blocking the road'. (NOT 'were blocking'; the herd is the subject, not the cattle, and there is only one herd, so the verb stays in the singular.)

It is sometimes possible to use a plural verb after a collective noun in the singular, — when there is a suggestion that the action is being taken by the individuals that make up the group. This sounds rather complicated, but look at how it works in these examples:—

'The jury *were* divided in *their* opinions about the police evidence, and *they* were unable to reach a verdict.' (Here we are thinking of the jury in terms of the men and women who are on it, so it is correct to have a plural verb, and to go on to refer to the jury as 'they' rather than 'it'.)

'The jury *was* out for sixteen hours in the big murder trial. In this important case the jury *consists* of eight women and four men.' (In these two sentences 'jury' is a simple collective noun, and since it is singular it must have a singular verb.)

When a singular collective noun has a plural sense in the way we have seen, it is sometimes known as 'a noun of multitide'. It is quite common now to use a plural verb after words like 'the government' and 'the committee', — but make sure, if you do so, that what you have written sounds right, and makes sense!

It is sometimes hard to see exactly what the subject of a particular verb is. It is easy to make a verb that should be singular into a plural, because there is a plural noun next to it:—

'A procession of buses, lorries and other assorted vehicles are moving down the street.' (Here 'procession' is the singular subject, acting like a collective noun, but because all the 'assorted vehicles' are plural, and they are much nearer to the verb, the verb has become plural too. This is wrong. The verb should be *is*, not *are*).

The same thing can happen to verbs in pieces of description which are added to sentences, but where it is not always clear at first who or what is actually being described:—

'We can see the long line of waiting vehicles, which stretch round the town square.' (Here the verb *stretch* is wrong; it should be *stretches* (singular). The 'line' is the subject, and since it is singular, its verb must also be singular; in other words, the line is stretching, not the vehicles — they all remain the same length!)

When you extend a singular subject with a description, *even if that description adds in some other item(s)*, the subject cannot become plural because of the extra description:—

'The general, with his whole army, *is* going to surrender.'

(Here even the appearance of a whole army could not make the verb plural!)

The same applies when you add to the subject with a connective like 'together with' or 'as well as' or 'in addition to':—

'Luke, as well as Steve, *is* responsible.' (*NOT* 'are' responsible.)

On the other hand, when you have two or more separate and equal things joined by AND as the subject of the verb, then the verb is plural, — since you have obviously got a plural subject. So if we change the above examples round a little, we have:—

'The general *and* his whole army *are* going to surrender.'

'Luke *and* Steve *are* responsible.'

The exception is when you have two words joined by 'and' that really stand for one and the same thing; then they are treated as one, and have a singular verb:—

'The dictator and tyrant of Europe *is* dead.' (He is only one person!)

'Fruit and vegetables *is* my business.' ('Fruit and vegetables' is treated as a single thing, so the verb is singular.)

When you have two singular subjects linked by OR (and by 'either . . . or . . ./neither . . . nor . . .') the verb is singular. EITHER, NEITHER and EACH are always singular; BOTH is plural!

'Either Claire or Emily *is* coming on the trip. Each of them *has* permission. Both *are* old enough.'

NOTE:— 'You and I'; 'He and I'; 'the dog and I' all count as *WE*; and in the same way 'You and he'; 'You and Mrs. Smyth' etc. all count as *YOU*.

(a) Insert the correct form of the verb from the choices given you in the brackets. Underline your answer.

(1) A flock of sheep (was/were) being driven to market.

(2) In those days there (was/were) herds of buffalo roaming the western plains.

(3) The committee (is/are) too large to do any useful work.

(4) The people (have/has) decided.

(5) The members of the electorate (have/has) made the final choice once again.

(6) The Chamber of Commerce (are/is) an important institution in this town.

(7) A host of angels (were/was) singing their eternal praises around the heavenly throne.

(8) The board of directors of Sadly & Split Ltd. (was/were) once again engaged in an acrimonious debate among themselves.

(9) The crew (was/were) already assembled on the fo'c'sle, and I soon discovered that their mood was an ugly one.

(10) A great mass of people surrounding the Prophet (were/was) stretching out eager hands to touch his face, his hands, even his robe.

(20)

(b) In these sentences some of the verbs do not agree with their subjects. Write out the sentences correcting the errors. Some questions may contain more than one mistake; some may not contain any. Underline any changes you make.

(1) A choice of apples, oranges, or bananas are available for dessert.

(2) Neatly arranged on the table were a collection of articles.

(3) There you will see a forest of mighty oaks which extend for almost fifty miles.

(4) The vivid light of the bonfires which has been lit on every hilltop illuminate the countryside far and wide.

(5) We shall never agree to terms of surrender which are so disdainful of our honour.

(6) The committee which have been deliberating all day shall announce its decision at four o'clock, when a statement will be issued to the press.

(7) That is a fine picture of horses which are hanging on the wall.

(8) The sight of all those chocolate cakes which meet his eyes are too much for William.

(9) It is then that Lieutenant Fuller and Sergeant Waters discover to their amazement that the whole vast army which was yesterday encamped upon the plain has today vanished as completely as if it had never been.

(20)

(c) In each of these sentences insert a form of the verb TO BE in the space shown.
Underline the word you have inserted. (You may find that more than one form can be used.)

(1) Jack and Jill .... going up the hill.

(2) Jack, together with Jill, ... going up the hill.

(3) Both .... going up the hill together.

(4) I see that you and Jill .... going up the hill today, Jack.

(5) Was it Jack or Jill who .... going up the hill?

(6) Neither Ben nor Douglas .... doing any work.

(7) Ben, as well as Douglas, ... misbehaving.

(8) Each of them .... being very lazy today.

(9) .... it you talking then, Douglas?

(10) Douglas admitted that it was he and Ben who .... talking.

(20)

FACTSHEET FOUR

SUBJECT & OBJECT

Just as a verb (in most uses) needs to have a subject, it *can* have an object.

The subject is the person, or thing, performing the action.

The object is the person, or thing, which receives the action.

Look at the simple little sentence: 'Ben is punching John.' There is a very obvious difference between the subject, who is performing the action ('Ben') and the object, who is receiving the action, — or having it done to him ('John')!

We can 'analyse' (i.e. break down into its component parts) this sentence like this:—

Subject:— *Ben*
Verb:— *is punching*
Object:— *John.*

In English the subject and object are shown simply by order. The subject is normally closely linked to the verb, and normally stands in front of the verb. Even in questions, where the subject and auxiliary verb reverse (e.g. Am I winning?) the subject is still in front of the main verb ('to win' in this particular example). Consider the difference in order in these two sentences; though the same words are used, the order reverses subject and object, and therefore reverses the meaning:—

(a)   The man is eating the fish. (Restaurant.)

(b)   The fish is eating the man. (Jaws.)

The personal pronouns have their own forms for their use as objects, rather than subjects, of sentences. You have already seen the subject forms, and been advised against mixing the two forms up. (See Factsheet One.) Here are the object forms:—

ME   HIM   HER   US   THEM.

Look at these examples of the different uses of pronouns as subject and object:—

'They (subj) were chasing (verb) them (obj).'

'She (subj) has been avoiding (verb) her (obj).'

NOTE (1) Verbal nouns — nouns formed from the parts of the verb — can themselves be the subject or object of the main verb in a sentence.

E.g. 'Good singing has always delighted me', where *singing* is a noun, and stands as the subject of the verb 'has delighted'.

'Have you heard the singing?', where *singing* is once again a noun, this time standing as the object of the verb 'have heard'.

These verbal nouns can themselves also have a kind of object attached to them (as in 'Flying a plane is great fun', where 'a plane' is acting as an object of the verbal noun 'flying'). When this happened a *noun phrase* is produced. You will learn more about phrases and other groups of words later. For now, it is enough to say that groups of linked words can act as the subject or object of a verb.

The other form of a verbal noun you often find as subject or object of a verb is the infinitive (*To do* etc.)

E.g. '*To fly* is great fun'.

NOTE (2) There is one form of the verb where there is apparently no subject: the IMPERATIVE — the form used for giving orders.

E.g. 'Listen!' 'Do this!' 'Follow me!' Two of these examples have obvious objects ('this' and 'me'), but none of them have a subject stated.

In imperatives, which are forms of talking to someone, we must *assume* there is an unstated subject, and that it is 'YOU!'

(a)   Rewrite the following sentences, reversing the meaning, by reversing the order of the subject and the object. (You may have to make some other changes.)

    (1)   Ben is punching that poor boy John again.

    (2)   Our dog has just bitten that strange man.

    (3)   We were about to attack the enemy.

    (4)   They have seen him walking down the street.

    (5)   Billy was always teasing the girls.

                                                                          (10)

(b)   For each of the new sentences you have written for (a), write out (1) the subject, and (2) the object. (Make it clear which is which when you write them out.)

                                                                          (10)

(c)   For each of the following sentences write out the SUBJECT, OBJECT, and VERB. Once again, make it clear which is which, — and remember that each of them may consist of more than one word.

    (1)   The man is eating the fish.

    (2)   The fish is eating the man.

    (3)   I have seen the light.

    (4)   You should have been turning the handle.

    (5)   Jenny studied the plan of the new store.

    (6)   The sudden appearance of the comet baffled the astronomers.

    (7)   The writing on the wall terrified the great king.

    (8)   Patrick's singing delights few people.

    (9)   The winner of this competition will be awarded the most spectacular prize yet seen on this show.

    (10) To remember old wrongs will engender the devising of new ones.

                                                                          (30)

(d)   Write out the following sentences, and underline all the verbal nouns (i.e. parts of verbs used as nouns). Some sentences may contain more than one; others may not have any.

    (1)   Does she know how to ride a bike?

    (2)   I heard the sound of running feet behind me.

    (3)   Your spelling needs a great deal of improvement, Zak.

    (4)   I was trying to read your writing yesterday.

    (5)   He heard the sound of the monks' voices raised in prayer.

    (6)   Ella hopes to swim for the school.

    (7)   The endless waiting was making us all nervous.

    (8)   It was a matter of deciding whether to go or to stay.

    (9)   I think it is time that we should be going.

    (10) What strange imaginings were haunting her fevered imagination on that fateful night we shall never know now.

                                                                          (10)

(e)   For each of the above sentences, write down (i) the main finite verb, and (ii) its subject. You will find many verbs that are not finite of course; they were what you were looking for in the previous exercise. In numbers (9) and (10) you will also find more than one finite verb; in these two questions try to pick out the verbs (and their subjects) *which seem to be most important,* or on which the rest of the sentence depends.

                                                                          (20)

FACTSHEET FIVE

TYPES OF VERBS

In a sentence we may find three TYPES of verbs:— TRANSITIVE
INTRANSITIVE
AUXILIARY

A *transitive* verb is one where the action is carried over to an *object*.
An *intransitive* verb has *no object;* the action of the verb is complete in itself.

Most verbs can be used transitively or intransitively. The key decider is whether or not there is an object. Look at the examples:—

The sun is melting the ice.	(Verb 'is melting' is transitive — object 'the ice').
The ice is melting.	(Verb 'is melting' is intransitive — there is no object).
The plane flew high.	(Verb 'flew' is intransitive — there is no object).
The pilot flew the plane.	(Verb 'flew' is transitive — object 'the plane').

Some verbs are not normally transitive, such as 'I die', but even these can sometimes be used in a transitive manner. Look at these examples:—
'On the first night the actor died a death', and 'The winner ran a tactical race'.

Here 'death' and 'race' are the objects of 'died' and 'ran' respectively. This sort of object which is closely connected with the verb itself, or follows on automatically from it, is sometimes known as a 'cognate object'.

It is important to remember that the object of a verb, the thing or person receiving the action, must be just that, — a thing or person. In terms of parts of speech, the object must be a noun or pronoun, or a group of words that act as a noun.

Do not confuse adverbs attached to a verb with the object of the verb. — In the example above, 'The plane flew high', 'flew' is an intransitive verb; 'high' is not its object, because 'high' is not a thing; it is an adverb telling you where or how the plane flew. 'High' is not the 'thing' which received the action of the verb, and it obviously couldn't be!

You will also find sentences of this kind:— 'I was sitting *on the chair*'. In this example do not think that 'the chair' is the object of the verb ' was sitting'; 'on the chair' is a phrase explaining where the action was happening; the verb 'was sitting' is intransitive — and it is very difficult to think of a way it could be transitive!

Auxiliary verbs are the parts of verbs which 'assist' the main verb in forming the other tenses etc. The tenses are set out below as a reminder. Auxiliary verbs are in italics.

ACTIVE:			PASSIVE	
	Present	I like I *am* liking I *do* like		I *am* liked I *am being* liked
	Future	I *shall* like I *shall be* liking		I *shall be* liked
	Imperfect	I *was* liking		I *was being* liked
	Past	I liked I *did* like		I *was* liked
	Perfect	I *have* liked I *have been* liking		I *have been* liked
	Future Perfect	I *shall have* liked I *shall have been* liking		I *shall have been* liked
	Pluperfect	I *had* liked I *had been* liking		I *had been* liked.

There are also subjunctive/conditional forms: I *may* like; I *might* like; I *should* like; I *would* like; and other tenses can be formed using may/might (e.g. I *may have* liked) — as can passive forms (e.g. I *might be* liked).

(a)   Write down each of the following sentences, and at the end of each write down the VERB. Each sentence has only one verb, but it may of course consist of several words. Make sure you write down the whole of the verb (including its auxiliaries).

(1)   The plane sped low over the crowd.

(2)   They have appointed Mrs Leech as Senior Consultant.

(3)   Are you still waiting for Mira?

(4)   The usherette seated us in the back row with all the other courting couples.

(5)   Baby was seated in his high chair, crying as usual.

(6)   She lay there, asleep at last.

(7)   Just lay the table for me, please, dear.

(8)   There he lies, in the churchyard, forever.

(9)   I have never lied in my whole life.

(10) The ice on the river was slowly melting.

(11) The chairs were arranged in a neat row.

(12) Never do that again, Jonathan, you bad boy!

(13) Where have you put my socks, mum?

(14) You were seen in very suspicious circumstances, Jimmy.

(15) Have you ever heard such a load of old rubbish?

(16) Put your hands up, partner, real slow. (NB Don't copy the grammar of this sentence!).

(17) And don't reach for your gun!

(18) I cannot abide the playing of the bagpipes.

(19) But then, I have no ear for music.

(20) She has decided to resign from her position.

(20)

(b)   Go through the list of verbs you have written out for exercise (a); look carefully at their use in the sentences; then write down next to each verb whether it is TRANSITIVE or INTRANSITIVE.

(20)

(c)   Use each of the following verbs in a sentence of your own TRANSITIVELY (i.e. so that it has an OBJECT):—

(1)	fly	(3)	choose	(5)	hear	(7)	act	(9)	run
(2)	melt	(4)	put	(6)	open	(8)	sink	(10)	wave

(10)

(d)   Use each of the following verbs in a sentence of your own INTRANSITIVELY (i.e. so that, though other words may be added to the verb, it does NOT have an OBJECT):—

(1)	fly	(3)	sit	(5)	leave	(7)	sleep	(9)	bend
(2)	put	(4)	walk	(6)	read	(8)	decide	(10)	see

(10)

(e)   In each of these sentences underline the AUXILIARY VERBS. (You may of course find there are none in a sentence; you may find that some main verbs have more than one auxiliary; you may find that there is more than one main verb, — and hence perhaps several auxiliaries.)

(1)   Who has taken my pen?

(2)   I have been working all morning, and I have nearly finished.

(3)   Why did you telephone last night?

(4)   You should have been here, Joe. Then you would have seen it.

(5)   Do not write in the margin.

(6)   There he is, running down that alley! Will they be able to catch him?

(7)   What on earth have you been trying to do with that bicycle wheel, Marcia?

(8)   He is a man who never once in his whole life has been known to smile.

(9)   I have never found her an easy person to work with.

(10) Once this course of action had been decided on, there would be no turning back.

(10)

11

FACTSHEET SIX

OBJECTS AND COMPLEMENTS

As you have seen, the *object* is what receives the action of the verb.

There are some verbs, however, which are not quite 'actions', in particular the verb TO BE. There is no 'action' involved in the verb *to be* to carry over to an object; but there are certainly words that follow the verb *to be* in, the place you would expect an object. Look at this example:— 'Mary is a clever girl'. The words 'a clever girl' are in the place where you would expect an object, — yet there is no action which is being carried over to them. In fact 'Mary' and 'a clever girl' are the same person. Words that follow the verb *to be* in this way, telling you what the subject IS, are called the COMPLEMENT, because they 'complete' the verb.

The verb *to be* in all its different forms will always have a complement, never an object.

NOTE — Remember that the verb 'to be' is often found not by itself, but as an auxiliary to another main verb. In this case it is the main verb which determines whether the following words will be object or complement (or neither). Here we are only talking about the verb *to be* when it is standing by itself.

The complement of the verb *to be* is often an adjective.

Other verbs can also have a complement, — when the words that follow the verb are *the same* person or thing as the subject of the verb. The most common of these are verbs of SEEMING and BECOMING. In these examples the words underlined are complements, not objects.

E.g. I am becoming *very tired*. She seems *a nice girl*. It is getting *late*.

Something similar can also happen with some verbs of PERCEIVING or FEELING:—

E.g. I feel *tired*. It smells *fishy*. It feels *hard*. It tasted *delicious*.

The way to decide object or complement is to see if the subject is the same person or thing as the words in doubt; if it is, then the words are complement, not object.

Some verbs can take two objects, of different sorts. All the objects we have used as examples so far have been DIRECT OBJECTS. The action of the verb carries over *directly* to the object.

Now look at these examples, particularly the words in italics in them:-

E.g. I sent *him* a letter. Somebody find *me* a bucket. Mark bought *his wife* a washing machine.

If you think about it, the thing being sent in the first example is a letter, not 'him'; in the second the thing being found is a bucket, not 'me'; in the third the thing being bought is a washing machine, not 'his wife'.

The words in italics are the people TO or FOR whom the action is being done. They benefit from the action, but they do not directly receive it themselves. They are in fact the INDIRECT OBJECTS of the verb.

The way to check whether a word or words are being used as indirect object is to see if you can insert TO or FOR in front of them, and still keep the sense.

You may also have noticed that the indirect object always comes first, before the direct object.

One final point on objects concerns verbs in the PASSIVE.

In passive verbs, the action is carried back to the subject. (E.g. 'The dress is being made', where 'The dress' is the subject of the verb, but is also the thing that is having the action done to it!)

So passive verbs will normally be intransitive; — they will not have an object.

There is an exception to this when a verb in the active voice has two objects (one direct and one indirect). Then, if the sentence is turned into the passive, one of them can stay.

E.g. 'Mr Cook taught the Juniors English':— *Active form*, where 'the Juniors' is the indirect object. — 'The juniors were taught English by Mr Cook': — *Passive Form*, but with an object — 'English'.

(a) Write out the following sentences and underline all the COMPLEMENTS.
  (1) If they don't hurry, they will be late.
  (2) Jane was the laziest girl in the class.
  (3) The teachers were all getting angry with her.
  (4) Your book is becoming very scruffy, Kevin.
  (5) Who on earth is he?
  (6) We all felt uneasy about the whole thing.
  (7) The entire project sounds quite impossible.
  (8) He has frequently been caught with his fingers in the till.
  (9) I was unhappy with the whole affair, but Tom voted in favour, and Jack was all for it.
  (10) Despite his awful childhood, Harry has emerged an honest man.

(10)

(b) Write out the following sentences. At the end of each write the OBJECT or COMPLEMENT of the verb. Say whether what you have written is the object or the complement. Remember that not all verbs *must* have objects or complements.
  (1) I carefully placed the letter on the window-sill.
  (2) Writing both neatly and quickly at the same time is very difficult.
  (3) Don't do it, Anne.
  (4) Are you going to be late again tomorrow, David?
  (5) To be or not to be, that is the question.
  (6) I felt the surface of the strange rock.
  (7) The Juniors were taught English by Mr Cook.
  (8) English was taught to the Juniors by Mr Cook.
  (9) Though the lasagne tasted delicious at the time, it made me very sick later on.
  (10) As the fire burnt steadily in the grate and the shadows lengthened imperceptibly across the floor, I was becoming very tired.

(20)

(c) In each of these sentences there is both an OBJECT and an INDIRECT OBJECT. Write both of them out in each case, and say which is the object and which the indirect object.
  (1) Mum bought Sally the rabbit.
  (2) The headmaster gave Oliver a stern lecture.
  (3) Mr Cook teaches the Juniors English.
  (4) Jeeves brought Bertie another sherry.
  (5) Though I sent it him by first class post, apparently it never arrived.

(20)

(d) In the following exercise write out each OBJECT, INDIRECT OBJECT, and COMPLEMENT you find, and carefully label each one to say whether it is complement, object or indirect object. You may find more than one of each in some of the sentences, and you may even find none at all.
  (1) When dad gave Douglas a smack, it did not feel very nice.
  (2) He traced a pattern with his finger in the sand.
  (3) Go on, Basher, give him one on the nose!
  (4) He made her a banana split, which was her favourite.
  (5) Never trust someone whose eyebrows are too close together.
  (6) The sun was sinking slowly towards the horizon.
  (7) Though it looked an easy problem, in the end it proved quite impossible.
  (8) He gave me a look to freeze the blood, his face went pale, and he raised his fist.
  (9) Give me another slug of whisky, bartender; I'm feeling thirsty.
  (10) You may wait as long as you like; I will never come back.

(30—1½ each)

13

FACTSHEET SEVEN

CLAUSES, PHRASES, AND SENTENCES

Though you are familiar with using sentences, it is worth defining what we mean by the word 'sentence'.

A SENTENCE is a group of words which makes complete sense by itself, and does not need the addition of any other words to explain it further.

Each sentence is marked by being given a capital letter to start it, and a full stop at the end. Normally a sentence will contain at least a subject and a verb, — though there are cases when they do not. — So long as a sentence makes complete sense, it *is* a sentence.

For example, sentences with verbs in the imperative (commands) do not have a stated subject, as in 'Do not touch it!' and 'Begone!' 'Notice that you can have sentences that consist of single words. This can also happen with the question words:— 'Why?' and 'When?' can stand as sentences in their own right. The same is true of 'Yes!' and 'No!'

Notice that exclamation marks and question marks are variations of a full stop, and are also used to end sentences.

As well as sentences, there are two other kinds of GROUP OF WORDS. They are:—

CLAUSES and PHRASES.

A CLAUSE is:— a group of words similar to a sentence, but not standing by itself
a group of words forming part of a sentence
similar to a sentence in that it must contain a FINITE VERB.

Very often, but not always, a clause could be a sentence by itself if it were taken out of the larger sentence and given its own capital letter and full stop.

Remember, a finite verb is a verb which tells you the main action occurring; — unless it is giving a command, it will have a *subject* (the thing or person performing the action) stated.

A PHRASE is:— a group of words forming part of a sentence
a group of words that cannot stand by itself and make complete sense
unlike a sentence in that it does NOT contain a finite verb.

A phrase cannot normally stand as a sentence by itself if it is taken out of the sentence in which it occurs. It will always need additional words added to complete its sense.

Though phrases do not contain finite verbs (telling you the main action and having a stated subject), they do very often contain nouns and adjectives formed from verbs — the forms of the present participle (ending in -ING) and the past participle (often ending in -ED), and the infinitive (TO do etc.)

When you are reading, you can test for particular groups of words being sentences, clauses or phrases relatively easily. If a group of words has a capital letter and full stop it is clearly intended to be a sentence. (You may, however, now you know the difference between these three types of word groups, decide that the writer should not have used a particular group of words as a sentence, and that, because it does not make complete sense, it is really only a phrase!)

A clause can be identified by having a finite verb, and being part of a larger sentence; see if it could stand by itself as a sentence.

A phrase simply will not make sense by itself; you need more information to complete it.

Here are some examples:—

'You turn left, and then you must go up the hill'. (Sentence, with two clauses.)

'I want to see the person *who wrote this*.' (Sentence with a clause (in italics) attached).

'*Understanding this page* is completely simple.' (Sentence with a phrase (in italics) as its subject).

'*By reducing the length* we could get two *out of the same piece*.' (Sentence with two phrases (in italics) attached.)

(a) Say whether the following groups of words are sentences or not. Write out each one, giving those that are sentences their full stops (or question marks, or exclamation marks) and capital letters. For each answer write SENTENCE or NOT SENTENCE at the end.

(1) a group of words similar to a sentence but without a main verb

(2) yes, we have no bananas

(3) whether they had gone or not

(4) to be caught in the narrow part of a cave, even without the water rising steadily around your legs, is bad enough

(5) was waiting for them at the top of the steps

(6) with a rush and a roar and a sudden jerk, as the train came to an abrupt stop

(7) who's that

(8) if only I had never gone to town on that fateful day

(9) o Mary, this London's a wonderful sight

(10) with the people here working by day and by night

(20)

(b) In each of the following sentences, as well as the main clause there is one or more additional clause, which adds further description or information. Write out these additional clauses (NOT the main clause) for each question.

(1) That's the one who did it, governor!

(2) We waited there in the darkness, until the church clock struck ten.

(3) If you do not own up now, you will be dealt with more severely.

(4) I do not know where he has gone.

(5) She wore a long swirling gown which had been embroidered with countless tiny jewels.

(6) How can we continue the fight when our leader has betrayed us?

(7) Though Adam said it was his, I knew for a fact that it really belonged to Mark. (TWO)

(8) He spoke at length on the subject, but to an audience who had already made up their minds, whatever he might choose to say. (TWO)

(20)

(c) Write out each phrase in the following sentences. Be careful, because you may find more than one phrase in a sentence, and you may find none at all. Do not confuse clauses and phrases; it is only phrases that are required this time.

(1) I will now make this banana disappear, before your very eyes.

(2) By your own unaided efforts you have saved this company from utter financial ruin, Mrs Weston.

(3) Beneath the moon and stars they met again.

(4) Out of the night came a soulless wailing cry.

(5) If you are not there when I want you, you can expect that I will dismiss you.

(6) Without a thought he sprang, with all his clothes still on, into the raging tide, striking out bravely for the struggling child.

(20)

(d) Write out the words in italics in the following sentences, and say whether they are CLAUSES or PHRASES.

(1) The decision *to accept the tender of Messrs. Grabbit & Runne* has proved an expensive one *for this firm.*

(2) *Wherever we hide* they will come, *as silent as the night,* and will wreak their dreadful vengeance.

(3) *Whoever is in there* had better come out, *before I come in and get them.*

(4) *Beside the three girls and Mrs Ponsonby, who is hardly a small woman,* we have to fit five suit-cases *into the back of this car, before we can set off.* (FOUR)

(10)

FACTSHEET EIGHT

TYPES OF SENTENCE

Sentences fall into two basic categories:— SIMPLE and COMPLEX.

Unfortunately, though, not all simple sentences are that simple!

The basic form of a simple sentence is — SUBJECT + PREDICATE.

The PREDICATE is all the rest of the sentence that is not part of the subject. It must contain the verb, and it may contain the object, or the complement, additions to the verb (adverbs or adverbial phrases), an indirect object if there is one, and so on.

So the basic form of the simple sentence is as in 'Peggy is flying her kite', where the subject is 'Peggy'; and the predicate 'is flying her kite' consists of a verb 'is flying' and an object 'her kite'.

'Being an international star is not a life to be recommended lightly' is also an example of a 'simple' sentence. It does not look simple because its subject is a long phrase — 'Being an international star', and its object 'life' has a descriptive phrase 'to be recommended lightly' added to it. Even so, you will see that the basic *subject — verb — object* form is still there.

From the simple sentence there are two natural developments — the DOUBLE and MULTIPLE sentence.

In these you have two or more simple sentences, joined together with a conjunction to make a single longer sentence. Each of the sentences is itself simple in form, and neither depends on the other. You could separate them very simply by taking away the conjunctions, and putting in extra capital letters and full stops at the breaks.

'I do not like that dress at all, Joan, and that hat is unbelievable' is an example of a double sentence. It is two sentences joined by 'and'; it could easily be divided to make:—

'I do not like that dress at all, Joan. That hat is unbelievable.'

In this example — 'Writing English text books is hard work, but teaching horrible children is even worse, and having a horrible teacher is the worst of all' we have a multiple sentence, — three equal sentences joined together by the conjunctions *and* and *but*. Each of the three parts of the multiple sentence has a complicated subject ('Writing English text books'; 'teaching horrible children'; 'having a horrible teacher'), but the form of each is still the simple Subject + Predicate.

(Did you notice that in each case the predicate was the verb TO BE + COMPLEMENT?)

NOTE that in some multiple sentences, where the subject of each verb is the same, it may be missed out the second or third time, as in 'She said farewell, and then departed' where the second 'she' (subject of 'departed') is missed out, as it is obvious who departed!

A COMPLEX sentence is once again a sentence with two or more parts. This time, however, one of the parts is the MAIN CLAUSE, while the other is the SUBORDINATE CLAUSE. The two parts are not equal; the subordinate part depends on the main part. You can see it best in examples:—

I am well aware what you are doing. (Main clause:— 'I am well aware'; Subordinate Clause:— 'what you are doing').

Jackie had no idea (MAIN) when her sister would arrive (SUBORDINATE).

After they had been dealt with by their fathers (SUBORDINATE) both Patrick and Douglas regretted their misbehaviour (MAIN).

Robin told Elizabeth (MAIN) that she was completely mistaken (SUBORDINATE).

Whoever is responsible for all this mess (SUBORDINATE) had better see me at break (MAIN).

(a) Divide these simple sentences into subject and predicate. (Make it clear which is which!)

    (1) Mrs Hale is our best teacher.

    (2) Steve has saved thirteen pounds from his birthday money.

    (3) Overcome at last by the enormity of his numerous crimes, he shot himself.

    (4) The plane, with both its engines now blazing, fell like a stone out of the sky.

    (5) This year's summer collection has not been without its surprises.

(10)

(b) Divide these simple sentences into SUBJECT, VERB, and OBJECT OR COMPLEMENT. Make it clear which is which. Remember to say whether there is an object or a complement. If there is no object or complement, write 'No object or complement'.

    (1) That boy, James, is an absolute idiot.

    (2) Have you seen the ghost?

    (3) We might all have been killed!

    (4) The task of appointing a new supervisor seems fraught with difficulties.

    (5) The 'Factories Act' does provide adequate procedures for claiming compensation.

(10)

(c) Divide up these double and multiple sentences into the simple sentences which are their component parts. (You may have to make various changes and additions in the process.)

    (1) I cannot stop you going, and I have no intention of trying to do so.

    (2) You can rely on Sam, but I am not so sure about Eliza.

    (3) Stuart rushed down the drive and struggled to open the gate, but the sound of running footsteps was already loud behind him.

    (4) You must either do it yourself, or alternatively get someone to come in to do it and pay him the market rate for the job.

(You should have found a total of ten separate sentences in the four above.)

(20—2 per sentence)

(d) Write out these sentences, and classify them as SIMPLE, DOUBLE, MULTIPLE or COMPLEX.

    (1) After you have changed, you must meet father.

    (2) After her terrifying experience, Jackie reached the safety of her cabin with relief.

    (3) He turned and fired again and again, but their numbers were too great, and within moments they were upon him.

    (4) I pointed out to him that the main propellor shaft had been bent.

    (5) You and I will have to do it, but it won't be easy.

(10)

(e) Divide these complex sentences up into MAIN and SUBORDINATE CLAUSES. Make sure you carefully label which is which. Be careful, because the clauses may be tangled up with each other, and you may find more than one subordinate or main clause in a sentence!

    (1) Inspector Sparkes, a persistent but unintelligent policeman, was determined that his suspect knew where the murder weapon was.

    (2) Despite the rigour of the interrogation, Derek, who was innocent of any crime, refused to admit anything.

    (3) Of course there had been no murder as yet, but the accused man felt the net of circumstantial evidence closing around him, however much he protested his innocence.

    (4) That is the reason he had to kill the inspector.

(20—2 per clause)

(f) Join these sentences into as FEW larger sentences — complex, or multiple — as you can. Complex sentences are preferable to multiple, — and it is possible to make ONE sentence.

    She was running happily down the street. She was singing cheerfully. The shopping basket swung from her hand. Then she tripped over the kerb. The carton of eggs came out of the basket. The eggs flew everywhere. Some of them landed on her head. They broke. She was covered in egg. She started to cry.

    (You can make changes as drastic as you like in doing this, so long as you preserve every part of the original SENSE; it is quite an entertaining puzzle!)

(10)

17

FACTSHEET NINE

TYPES OF CLAUSE AND PHRASE

Clauses and phrases can be classified according to the work they do in the sentence, in exactly the same way as individual words can be classified. The main types are set out below.

A NOUN CLAUSE or NOUN PHRASE. These are clauses or phrases which do the work of nouns — they stand for 'things' for the most part, and in particular the sort of 'things' which fall into the 'abstract' category. So a noun clause or noun phrase can be:—

The SUBJECT of a verb, as in *'Writing good English* is very difficult'. (Noun phrase).
'That the victim was murdered is not in doubt'. (Noun clause).

The OBJECT of a verb, as in 'You should practise *your writing of longer sentences.'* (Phrase).
'We are pleased to announce *that we have appointed Mr. Briggs as managing director.'* (Clause).

A COMPLEMENT, after the verb to be, as in 'This result is exactly *what I expected'*. (Clause).

(Look at these examples, and notice the difference between the clauses and the phrases: you will remember that a clause has a finite verb, while a phrase does not).

AN ADJECTIVE CLAUSE or ADJECTIVE PHRASE. These are clauses or phrases which do the work of adjectives, — they describe, or 'qualify' a noun (or a noun phrase/clause!)

Adjective *clauses* are nearly always introduced by a relative pronoun (Who, which, what, that, whose, whom), and can equally be referred to as 'relative clauses'.

Here are some examples:—

The boy *with the red hair, cauliflower ear and long nose* was the culprit. (Adjective phrase, describing the noun 'boy'.)

Any boy *who can be recognized so easily* should stay out of trouble. (Adjective — or relative — clause, describing the noun 'boy'.)

Deciding on the flavour of the crisps, *which is always a source of disagreement*, today produced a full-scale battle between Mark and Adam. (Adjective clause qualifying or describing the NOUN clause 'deciding on the flavour of the crisps' — which is itself the subject of the main verb!)

NOTE that some relative clauses miss out their relative pronoun, as in 'The parcel *the postman delivered this morning* contained my books'. The relative clause is in italics, but its pronoun ('that' or 'which') has been left out. Only do this if it makes sense!

AN ADVERB (or ADVERBIAL) CLAUSE or ADVERBIAL PHRASE. These are clauses or phrases which do the work of adverbs, — they describe or 'modify' a verb (or sometimes an adjective). Just as with adverbs they answer the questions 'HOW, HOW MUCH, WHEN, WHERE, WHY?' Look at the examples:—

Paul came first *because he worked the hardest.*	Adverbial clause of Reason/Cause. (Answers the question WHY?)
I am excused games *because of my feet...!*	Adverbial phrase of Reason/Cause.
Most people eat *in order that they may live.*	Adverbial clause of Purpose (WHY? again.)
Derek lives *in order to eat.*	Adverbial phrase of Purpose.
Fools rush in *where angels fear to tread.*	Adverbial clause of Place. (WHERE?)
Under the spreading chestnut tree, we fell asleep.	Adverbial phrase of Place.
It stopped hurting *after an hour or so.*	Adverbial Phrase of Time. (WHEN?)
When the great bell tolls, break will be over.	Adverbial Clause of Time.
She made her way to school *as slowly as she could.*	Adverbial Clause of Manner (HOW?)
The vase fell to the floor *with an echoing crash.*	Adverbial Phrase of Manner.

Some other common adverbial clauses are known as 'Conditional' (IF), 'Concessive' (ALTHOUGH), and 'Comparative' (THAN etc.). For example:—

If you do well, you will get a reward.	Adverbial Clause of Condition.
Although I did well, I didn't get a reward.	Adverbial Clause of Concession.
He said I could have done better *than I did.*	Adverbial Clause of Comparison.

(a) For each of the following sentences write out the noun clause or phrase which it contains. Clearly say whether each one is a clause or a phrase.

    (1) It has been decided that you must die, Mr Bond.

    (2) We have always enjoyed listening to good music.

    (3) To release the prisoner was the work of a moment.

    (4) I will do what I can.

    (5) The skilful disposing of the body is always the mark of a really thoughtful murderer.

                                                                                  (10)

(b) In each of these sentences there is an adjectival clause or adjectival phrase. Write these out, and clearly state whether each is a clause or a phrase.

    (1) Look out for the man with the yellow eye-patch; he is the courier.

    (2) Voting for the new president, who will run the union for the next ten years, begins tomorrow.

    (3) This election, once the source of widespread controversy, is now conducted by secret ballot.

    (4) The song he was singing reminded Melissa of the old days.

    (5) Whoever is responsible has done damage to this organization which will not be repaired for many years.

                                                                                  (10)

(c) In each of the following sentences there is an adverbial phrase or clause. For each sentence write this out, say clearly whether it is a clause or phrase, and also state what type of adverbial clause or phrase it is — Reason, Purpose, Place, Time, Manner, Condition, Concession, Comparison.

    (1) After the clock had stopped there was no sound.

    (2) With a flying leap he sprang from the balcony.

    (3) I cannot come because the car has broken down.

    (4) Nothing is better than a large bowl of strawberries.

    (5) To lighten the balloon, we threw out the navigator.

    (6) If I can do this exercise, I can do anything.

    (7) In the centre of the arena, the dauntless gladiator awaited the lions.

    (8) Despite the extent of her injuries, she has made a dramatic recovery.

    (9) We all work hard so that we can improve our English.

    (10) Wait for me where we always used to meet.

                                                                                   (20)

(d) In the following passage each of the clauses and phrases has been underlined. Write out each of these, and next to each write the following information:—

    (1) Whether it is a clause or a phrase.

    (2) Whether it is a noun, adjective, or adverb clause or phrase.

    (3) If it is a NOUN clause or phrase, whether it is subject, object, or complement.
    If it is an ADJECTIVE clause or phrase, what word it qualifies or describes.
    If it is an ADVERB clause or phrase, what type it is.

    James closed the switch <u>with considerable difficulty</u>. He knew <u>what to do next</u>. <u>After he had checked the temperature gauge,</u> <u>which was calibrated</u> <u>with a whole series of figures</u>, he set the programme <u>for the chosen operation</u>. The only remaining task was <u>to press the start control</u>. <u>Though he did so</u>, nothing happened. <u>After a moment</u> he pressed the button again. It was no good. <u>Operating a piece of advanced technology</u> was simply too hard.

    "Mum, how do you turn the washing machine on?" he called.

                                                                                           (30)

FACTSHEET TEN

SENTENCE ANALYSIS

You now know enough about the structure of sentences and their component parts to be able to analyse them. 'Analyse' simply means to split something up into its different parts to find out what they are.

The first piece of splitting up we can do is to divide the sentence into:—

(a) SUBJECT   The person or thing performing the action, and

(b) PREDICATE All that follows from the subject; the main (finite) verb, anything added to the verb to describe it further — an adverb or an adverbial phrase or clause — the object, indirect object, or complement (if any) and anything added to them as additional description.

The next stage is equally simple; we can divide the predicate into:—

(c) VERB (the main or finite verb; remember it may consist of several words).

(d) Additions to the verb.

A category called 'additions to the verb' is obviously not very useful, and needs to be split up into what those additions are. They fall into two categories. Firstly there are words or phrases you need to complete the verb. If it is a transitive verb it will have an object. (Look back at Factsheet Four if you are unsure about transitive/intransitive verbs.) If it is a verb of 'being' etc. it will have a complement instead. It may be a verb that has an indirect as well as a direct object. (You may want to check Factsheet Five as well about what exactly these terms mean.) The second category is that of simple additions to the verb itself, — adverbs or adverbial phrases, that 'modify' the verb. So now we have a new and smaller category (d), plus a new category:—

(e) Completion of the Verb — consisting of object (direct and indirect) or complement.

Here are three sentences as examples, followed by their analysis according to the plan we have just worked out:—

(1) The intelligent girl wrote an excellent essay about space flight in her English book.

(2) The girl's teacher was very pleased with her work.

(3) She immediately gave her top marks and a star for effort.

	(a) SUBJECT	(b) PREDICATE		
		(c) VERB	(d) ADDITIONS TO VERB	(e) COMPLETION OF VERB
1)	The intelligent girl	wrote	in her English book	OBJECT—an excellent essay about space flight
2)	The girl's teacher	was	—	COMPLEMENT—very pleased with her work
3)	She	gave	immediately	DIRECT OBJ.—top marks and a star for effort INDIRECT OBJ.-her

There are a few things worth noticing about these particular examples:—

In (1) the addition to the verb is an adverbial phrase. (It answers the question WHERE?).

In (2) there is a complement, rather than an object, because the verb is the verb TO BE.

In (3) there is a direct object (the thing that was given), and also an indirect object (the person TO whom it was given).

(a) Analyse the following sentences into SUBJECT and PREDICATE. (Do not try to divide the predicate up any further.)

    (1) The light of the moon filled the empty room.

    (2) I walked with a steady and unwavering pace through the howling mob and up the steps towards the awaiting guillotine.

    (3) That boy with the ginger hair, blue eyes and a mass of freckles, who used to live in our street at number thirty-eight, has just got married.

    (4) Whoever could have done such a thing?

    (5) Surely you have not all deserted me?

(10)

(b) Analyse the following sentences into SUBJECT, VERB and REST OF PREDICATE.

    (1) I gave my bags to the porter to put on the down train.

    (2) It should have been destroyed.

    (3) Ted has finally decided to get a job.

    (4) A good general always considers his army's welfare.

    (5) Will you be wanting this file now?

    (6) Stamp collecting as a hobby has its merits.

    (7) To write a decent song is easier than to sing one.

    (8) Max should if possible at that point have left immediately.

    (9) A dull haze, shimmering in the last of the endless day's ennervating heat, was rising imperceptibly up the long slopes of the beach and into the tall groves of palm trees above.

   (10) Never in the history of human conflict has so much been owed by so many to so few.

(20)

(c) Analyse the following sentences as fully as you can, dividing them into subject and predicate, and the predicate into: verb; additions to the verb; completion of the verb.

    (1) Paula was definitely wearing purple eye-shadow.

    (2) The supervisor praised Nasim's work again today.

    (3) There is no excuse for laziness.

    (4) Miss Stevens would never have tolerated that sort of thing.

    (5) After the fire, the house was no more than a blackened shell.

    (6) The hunted creature suddenly gave a shrill cry of utter terror.

    (7) Far too many teachers seem unable to control their pupils in class.

    (8) They have sent me a parcel of books.

    (9) Are you the naughty boy with the pea-shooter?

   (10) Come here at once!

   (11) It should have been finished by tomorrow morning.

   (12) The establishment of yet another committee will hardly help the situation.

   (13) Silently and stealthily, the long sinuous shape of the great serpent coiled itself round the base of the sleeping girl's chair.

   (14) My pleasure in presenting this handsome gift is qualified only by my regret at the departure of so distinguished a colleague.

   (15) Struggling there on the parapet of the bridge, high above the swirling waters, her very life in peril, Karen at last gave her masked and cloaked attacker a hefty kick on the shins, enough to send him staggering back towards the awaiting edge and the darkness beneath.

(60)

FACTSHEET ELEVEN

SENTENCE ANALYSIS (2)

The next stage in sentence analysis is a relatively simple development from what you have already done.

Look at these three new examples:—

(1)   The plane with smoke pouring from its engine was diving steeply towards the airfield.

(2)   From the control tower, in those last moments, we all saw the terror-stricken face of the young pilot.

(3)   The poor fellow, given the strength of desperation, had somehow opened the stiff perspex hood of the cockpit.

In analysing these sentences we need to start by finding the subject — who or what is carrying out the action of the verb. What we find is that the subjects in numbers (1) and (3) are rather long:—

(1)   SUBJECT:— The plane with smoke pouring from its engine....

(3)   SUBJECT:— The poor fellow, given the strength of desperation....

What we have in these cases is a great deal of description added to the subject. We need to break it down further (i.e. to analyse it!) into SUBJECT WORD, and the additions or extensions to the subject word.

What we then get is:—

(1)   SUBJECT WORD:—Plane
     EXTENSIONS:—   The
     With smoke pouring from
     its engine

(3)   SUBJECT WORD:—Fellow
     EXTENSIONS:—   The
     Poor
     Given the strength of
     desperation.

Notice how you can improve the clarity by setting out each separate extension on its own line. (This is worth doing with separate 'additions to the verb' as well.)

Exactly the same sort of thing needs to be done with the object or complement of the verb.

In these examples, sentence number (1) has no object; its verb is intransitive. But in numbers (2) and (3) there are long objects:—

(2)   OBJECT:— The terror-stricken face of the young pilot.

(3)   OBJECT:— The stiff perspex hood of the cockpit.

This time we can separate out the 'object word' and the extensions to it as follows:—

(2)   OBJECT WORD:— Face
     EXTENSIONS:—   The
     Terror-stricken
     Of the young pilot.

(3)   OBJECT WORD:— Hood
     EXTENSIONS:—   The
     Stiff perspex
     Of the cockpit.

We can now do a complete analysis of the three sentences.:—

	(a) SUBJECT	(b) PREDICATE		
		(c) VERB	(d) ADDITIONS TO VERB	(e) COMPLETION OF VERB
(1)	SUBJ. WORD: plane EXTENSIONS: the with smoke pouring from its engine	was diving	steeply towards the airfield	—

(2)	SUBJ. WORD: we
	EXTN. all
		saw	from the control tower
			in those last moments
				DIRECT OBJECT
				OBJ. WORD: face
				      the
				      terror-stricken
				      of the young pilot

(3)	SUBJ: fellow
	EXTN: the
	      poor
	      given the
	strength of desperation
		had opened	somehow	DIRECT OBJECT
				OBJ WORD: hood
				EXTN: the
				      stiff perspex
				      of the cockpit

The precise way you set out a sentence analysis is not important, so long as you make it as clear as possible. You may find ways of improving clarity; if you do, use them. (One way included in the above is to underline the subject and object words — and also the main verb.)

(a) Pick out the subject from each of the following sentences. Write it out in full, and then divide it up into SUBJECT WORD and EXTENSIONS. (Remember the and a are extensions.)

(1) The sky was filled with dark clouds.

(2) A steady drizzle had been falling all night.

(3) The light of the sun hardly managed to break through at all.

(4) More scudding clouds, heavy with the promise of new rain yet to come, gathered on the horizon.

(5) In fact, it was a typical English summer's day.

(6) The collection of mediaeval sculpture, recently presented to the museum by Sir Joshua Bullstrode and now housed in the Bullstrode Gallery, has been the object of much public interest.

(7) After hearing of the seriousness of the case, despite the lateness of the hour, Dr Reilly, never one to be remiss in her duty, took her bag and left the house for Trumpington Street.

(8) Relying, as always, on his cavalry, the general gave the signal for an advance against the artillery positions on the ridge above.

(9) Relying on cavalry in modern warfare is neither appropriate nor wise.

(10) What on earth has that silly man done to my cheese-grater?

(20)

(b) From the following sentences pick out OBJECT, INDIRECT OBJECT and COMPLEMENT; state which of these the word or phrase is; then divide them up into OBJECT WORD (or INDIRECT OBJECT WORD or COMPLEMENT WORD) and EXTENSIONS. If there is NO object, indirect object or complement in a sentence, say so. If there is both an object and an indirect object, make sure that you list both. Set out your answers in the clearest way you can.

(1) I do dislike the rain.

(2) Well, have you seen this cheese-grater, then?

(3) William is always lazy.

(4) However, he is not the laziest boy in the class.

(5) Suddenly, at the window, I too saw the dreadful face of the ghost.

(6) She was running with all her might towards the distant tape.

(7) I have sent young Johnny that parcel of toys.

(8) Through the mist, I suddenly caught, just for a moment, the faintest glimpse of the landing strip beneath us.

(9) Write me a letter, won't you, Joe?

(20)

(c) Analyse the following sentences fully, in the way set out at the bottom of the Factsheet opposite.

(1) I have no time now.

(2) Those three boys were climbing my apple tree again this morning.

(3) That ginger-haired one, Stuart, is the worst of them.

(4) He is always pinching the apples from my tree.

(5) One day I shall catch him at it though.

(6) Then I shall give him a nasty surprise.

(7) Who will buy my red roses?

(8) Do you see that faint light flickering in the window there?

(9) With an athletic leap the agile young hero siezed the wildly swaying chandelier.

(10) Swinging across the length of the room, scattering the guards with his flailing feet, he suddenly and heavily collided with the far wall.

(40)

FACTSHEET TWELVE

ANALYSIS OF COMPLEX SENTENCES (1)

You may well think that the analysis has already become complex enough, but in fact all the sentences we have analysed on the previous two factsheets were SIMPLE sentences. They had only a single finite verb, there were no conjunctions adding on additional sections to make the sentence double or multiple; there were no subordinate CLAUSES. They were LONG — but only because there were long descriptions in the form of phrases added to the subject, object and verb.

Firstly, then, how de we go about analysing a DOUBLE or MULTIPLE sentence? Since it has TWO or more MAIN CLAUSES, it seems reasonable to separate them out at the start, say what each of them is, and state the word or words that link them together.

Look at these two examples of double sentences to see how the analysis is set out:—

(1)   You have made the wrong decision, but I shall still support you.

(2)   She took the little baby and rocked it gently in her arms.

	CLAUSE	CLAUSE TYPE	CONNEC-TION	SUBJECT	PREDICATE		
					VERB	ADDITIONS TO VERB	COMPLETION OF VERB
(1)	You have made the wrong decision	MAIN (1)	—	You	have made	—	OBJ: decision EXT: the wrong
	I shall still support you	MAIN (2)	but	I	shall support	still	OBJ: you
(2)	She took the little baby	MAIN (1)	—	She	took	—	OBJ: baby EXT: the little
	rocked it gently in her arms	MAIN (2)	and	(she)	rocked	gently in her arms	OBJ: it

NOTICE that in the second main clause of number two where the subject is the same as in the first half of the sentence, it has not been repeated, so we show it in the analysis in brackets.

A COMPLEX sentence is one that has more than one part again; but this time there are not two or more equally important clauses; instead there are clauses which are dependent on, or SUBORDINATE to, the main clause.

We can use the same format as for a double sentence, so long as we make it clear exactly what the subordinate clauses are doing in the sentence.

Once again, it is probably easiest to see how to do it by examples:—

(3)   The news that mother was ill was a terrible shock.

(4)   The committee awarded the woman who had entered the best design a prize of £2,000.

	CLAUSE	CLAUSE TYPE	CONNEC-TION	SUBJECT	PREDICATE		
					VERB	ADDITIONS TO VERB	COMPLETION OF VERB
(3)	The news was a terrible shock	MAIN	—	News EXT: the PLUS ADJ. CLAUSE.	was	—	COMP: shock EXT: a terrible
	that mother was ill	ADJ.	that	mother	was	—	COMP: ill
(4)	The committee awarded the woman a prize of £2,000	MAIN	—	committee EXT: the	awarded	—	DIRECT OBJ: prize EXT: a of £2,000 INDIRECT OBJ: woman EXT: the PLUS ADJ. CLAUSE.
	who had entered the best design	ADJ.	who	(woman) who	had entered	—	OBJ: design EXT: the best

WORKSHEET TWELVE

(a) Analyse these double and multiple sentences in the way set out on the worksheet. You would be well advised to draw the analysis grid across a double page.

(1) I saw him, but he did not see me.

(2) Ben raced down the path, and James chased him.

(3) He is responsible, and I will not be told any excuses.

(4) Emma was climbing a tree, Sarah hammered nails into the dilapidated rabbit hutch, and Tom was quietly drawing in the sun-lounge.

(5) Either young Smithers has lost it, or you have.

(6) My hand touched the cold object, and I jumped in fright.

(7) I gave a sudden cry, but afterwards the silence seemed more total.

(8) For all his determination, he could not fight the establishment, and the establishment knew it.

(9) Mother fed the baby and then gave it a bath.

(10) Alison jumped on her uncle, gave him a punch in the chest, and then ran off giggling.

(11) My whole body was trembling violently, and even the slightest sound would have terrified me, but fortunately none came.

(12) Who is it, and what do you want?

(13) I make no bones about it:— this is not an easy job; and I will only be taking volunteers.

(14) Robin packed his tent, counted the poles and tent-pegs carefully, wrapped the whole lot up with the rest of his camping gear, and then put his bundle into the boot of the car.

(15) The dispatch department have sent the Hoo Mak Suds Laundry that consignment of new tee-shirts, and Bloggs Brothers, the clothing store, my dirty washing.

(45—3 each)

(b) Now analyse these complex sentences.

(1) After they heard the bell, the children all rushed into the playground.

(2) Flying a plane is simple, if you already drive a car.

(3) That girl who broke the window wants her ball back.

(4) She put the baby, which was crying again, in the pram, and hurried off down the road.

(5) Mr Sanders, who is always annoyed with the people in his class, teaches us Maths and Science.

(6) He gets so annoyed because we constantly misbehave in lessons.

(7) Though you have made the wrong decision, I shall still support you.

(8) The woman who won the prize had entered an excellent design.

(9) When I heard that mother was ill I was very shocked.

(10) I would not give him the time of day if he was the last person in the world, and I mean it too.

(11) We could not discover where he had hidden the documents though we questioned him all day.

(12) I went up to him, held out my hand, and, though we had been enemies for years, he shook it.

(13) He asked me if I had any means of identification, so I showed him my passport.

(14) "Can you see it too, or am I going mad?" I asked, as the monster surfaced again.

(15) British Rail apologizes to those passengers who are waiting for the eighteen thirty from Manchester, which, we are informed, is running ninety-three minutes late.

(45)

FACTSHEET THIRTEEN

ANALYSIS OF COMPLEX SENTENCES (2)

This Factsheet is really to set out again the things to remember when doing sentence analysis. Analysis of complex sentences is one of the hardest things to do in English. Quite often there is more than one way of looking at what a word or phrase is doing in a sentence. Essentially, if what you decide on makes sense, and fits in with the rules you have now learnt, you will not go far wrong. After all, professors of English can disagree about precise points of grammar!

How you set out an analysis of a sentence is one of the most important things about it. Try to be as clear as you can. Space the analysis out over a page or two pages. If you are varying the layout at all, make it very clear which category is which.

Once again, notice that by underlining subject, object(s) and main verb you can highlight the key words in the sentence, — the bare bones of its skeleton.

Divisions of Sentence:—

Subject:	The person or thing performing the action of the verb.
Verb:	The doing word, the statement of the main action.
Direct Object:	The person or thing which directly receives the action of the verb.
Indirect Object:	The person or thing for whom or to whom the action is transmitted.
Complement:	The equivalent of an object after verbs of being, becoming, etc. — completes these verbs.
Additions to Verb:	Adverbs, and adverbial clauses and phrases; not an object to a verb, not the recipient of the action, but additional descriptions of the manner, place, time etc. of the action itself.
Phrases:	Additions to subject, object, verb etc. which describe; phrases do not have a verb of their own.
Clauses:	Also descriptive additions to verb, subject, object etc., but this time having verbs of their own, and therefore needing their own separate analysis. Clauses (like phrases) can do the work of noun, adjective, or adverb.
Main Clause:	In a complex sentence, the main clause is the main part of the sentence — the chief piece of action. It has a main verb, with its subject (and object etc. if any). The other clauses are known as *subordinate clauses*; they add to one part or other of the main clause, — but are not usually essential to it.

Once again, the best way to learn how to do analysis is by looking at some examples:—

(1) *The light of the early dawn, as it spread over the hills, lit the vast and silent sea with a cold, unearthly glow.*

This time we will work through the process. The first thing to do is find the subject and the main verb:— *Light* (subj.); *lit* (verb). Describing the subject we have a phrase *of the early dawn*, — and a subordinate clause, which we leave for the time being. Next we see if there is an object (i.e. What, if anything, did the light light?!) The object is in fact *the sea*, and we have *vast and silent* as an extension to it. *With a cold unearthly glow* tells us the way the lighting was done; — it describes the manner of the verb as an adverb would, — so it is an addition to the verb.

Now, with the main clause analysed, we turn to the subordinate clause: *as it spread over the hills.* The connecting word is clearly *as*, and the rest of the clause is also simple. *It* is the subject; *spread* is the verb; *over the hills* tells us where it spread, so it is an addition to the verb; — it is not the object (since *the hills* are not being *spread*!)

(2) *If William gets a better mark in the maths exam than Steve got last year, Mr Cook, the teacher who is responsible for the Juniors, has promised to eat his best hat — without salt!*

This long sentence begins with a conditional ('if') clause, so that cannot be the main clause. When we do get to the subject of the main verb — *Mr Cook* — it is immediately followed by a descriptive word (*teacher*) and then a subordinate descriptive clause. The main verb when we finally get to it is *has promised*, and the object of the verb is an INFINITIVE *to eat*. The extension of this object, the words telling you more about it, are *his best hat* and *without salt*.

Now we can sort out the subordinate clauses. Firstly we have the conditional clause, with the connecting word *if*; *William* the subject; *gets* the verb; *a better mark* the object and its extension, — except that there is now another clause attached to the object — subordinate to a subordinate:— *than Steve did last year*. So we have to analyse that separately as well: connecting word *than*; subject *Steve*; verb *got*; additions to verb *last year*; — and no object. That only leaves the adjectival clause describing Mr Cook, the teacher:— *who* is the connecting word, and also the subject; *is* is the verb, and since it is part of the verb 'to be' it must have a complement — *responsible*, with *for the Juniors* as the extension of the complement. And that is it finished!

(a) Analyse the two examples used on the Factsheet, on the basis of the explanation given to you:—

(1) The light of the early dawn, as it spread over the hills, lit the vast and silent sea with a cold, unearthly glow.

(2) If William gets a better mark in the maths exam than Steve got last year, Mr Cook, the teacher who is responsible for the Juniors, has promised to eat his best hat — without salt.

(10)

(b) Analyse the following simple, double and multiple sentences:—

(1) The silly boy drew a picture of his father on the bedroom wall.

(2) The boy's father was extremely angry with him.

(3) The irate man tried to wipe it off, but he only rubbed a hole in the wallpaper and made an even worse mess.

(4) He gave his naughty son a jolly good hiding, and the boy howled loudly.

(5) That boy is unlikely to draw pictures on the wall again.

(10)

(c) Analyse the following complex sentences:—

(1) He praised those who were dead, and castigated the living.

(2) That is the castle where Mary Queen of Scots was beheaded.

(3) If you show me the samples you have prepared, I will give you an opinion on them.

(4) That there is an emergency is now very obvious to us all.

(5) When she left school, Tina started a training course in computer programming.

(6) If that happens, and it is very likely, then we are in trouble.

(7) It was too wet to go out, so we decided to play Scrabble.

(8) Although he is rather old, he is the only one who really understands the process.

(9) I hope that he does not intend to create a scene again tonight.

(10) Though all have abandoned me, I will remain true to my principles.

(20)

(d) Analyse the following complex sentences. (There is rather more to these examples!)

(1) The strike which had been called by the Amalgamated Union of Dustblowers and Threadneedlers is unlikely to affect production.

(2) What could we do when, after the curtain had gone up, he came on stage with a bottle of whisky in his hand and sang three choruses of 'I belong to Glasgow'?

(3) When the chairman had finished speaking we asked him repeatedly if he really intended to resign, but he declined to reply.

(4) When I say what I mean, I mean what I say.

(5) After they had eaten an enormous lunch and drunk their fill, the Board of Directors decided, in the interests of economy, to cut pay once again.

(6) After the debate had ended, the members filed into the different lobbies, and, when the count had been completed, it soon become clear that the government had been decisively defeated.

(7) Please consider what you have heard, and, when you have reached a verdict on which you are all agreed, elect a foreman who will deliver that verdict when you return to the courtroom.

(8) He said that there was no chance, but we could try if we really wanted to, after he had gone home, so long as he knew nothing about it.

(9) They gave no thought to time or place and hours flew by in that first careless moment when they met in the moonlight beside the ever-flowing stream.

(10) The secret police, whose incompetence was well-known, had once again arrested the wrong man, and had done this in a manner which would be unacceptable in a democratic society.

(40)

FACTSHEET FOURTEEN

DIRECT AND INDIRECT SPEECH(1)

This is a simpler topic than the analysis of sentences, but there are still some points which you will need to learn, and about which people very often make mistakes.

DIRECT SPEECH   This is the inclusion in a piece of writing of the ACTUAL WORDS which someone says.

The words must always be put inside *quotation marks* (also called *speech marks* or *inverted commas*).

Each time the speaker changes in a piece of dialogue (conversation), there must be a new PARAGRAPH (i.e. the words must be indented from the side of the page).

The words of saying (*he said, he replied* etc.) are NOT put inside the quotation marks; they are separated from the words spoken by a comma, or other punctuation mark.

Here are some examples of direct speech:—

(a)   "Are you coming out to play, Mary?" asked Pat.

(b)   "There is a suspicious object under that seat," said the passenger.

(c)   "You will have to fill out this form," muttered the clerk. "Put your full name and date of birth at the top."

(d)   "I have reached my decision," she snapped, "and there is nothing you or anyone else can do to stop me. — Now get out, all of you!"

Things to notice:- In (a) there is no comma after the words spoken because they end with a question mark.

In (c) where the speech re-starts after the full stop there is no new paragraph because it is the same person speaking.

In (d) the words telling you who spoke — *she snapped* — are put in the middle of the sentence being spoken. Since they are not part of the actual words they have to be separated off from the rest by commas, and most importantly by speech marks, which show that the words spoken end before and resume after these two words.

Here is an example of a piece of dialogue, where several people speak, and the rule requiring a new paragraph for each change of speaker comes into force:—

"Is that you, Peter?" said Mum, as she heard the door slam.

"Yes!" came a shout from downstairs, followed by another shout from the bathroom:—

"No, it's me, Steven. What do you want?"

"I don't mean you, Steven," Mum answered, "I mean Peter."

"Yes it is Peter," said Peter's voice from downstairs. "Did you want something?"

"No, nothing. I'm talking to Steven," answered Mum, getting a little exasperated.

"But you just told me you were talking to Peter," said Steven, and Peter shouted:—

"No, it's not Steven it's Peter......"

Obviously they have enough confusion already, since they never know who it is speaking! When we read the dialogue, however, we do not share this confusion, since the correct use of inverted commas and the paragraph rule, makes it clear exactly who is speaking.

The other form of reporting speech — INDIRECT SPEECH — which we will cover on the next Factsheet does NOT report the actual words. Do not put inverted commas round anything that is not the actual words spoken.

Beware of phrases like:— *He said that* . . .; He answered *that* . . .; *His reply was that* . . . They are common methods of introducing indirect speech. Just check the words that follow, — and see if they are the precise words spoken. If not, then they do not have inverted commas.

(a) Write out the following sentences, putting in the speech marks, and other pieces of punctuation required, where there is direct speech.

(1) I cannot see a thing I answered.

(2) Have you seen May anywhere I inquired.

(3) Come with me he commanded in a stern voice.

(4) Do you want another biscuit, Mark Mum asked.

(5) Do it at once Dad shouted and don't argue.

(6) It's only me, Mum, Jimmy called up the stairs.

(7) Your tea is on the table came the answer but wash your hands first.

(8) Have you seen my coat, Susan demanded Peter angrily.

(9) Write as much as you can the instructions stated, then hand in your paper.

(10) He was here a moment ago she said thoughtfully and looked all around but now he seems to have vanished altogether.

(20)

(b) Write out the following passage, putting in the speech marks, and any other punctuation that is missing. Remember that each time there is a change of speaker, you should start a new paragraph (as well as inserting speech marks and a capital letter).

Four candles please I said as the shopkeeper came over. Certainly, madam. How many would you like he asked. I looked puzzled, and then replied four. I did say four now it was his turn to look puzzled and scratch his head I'll just go and get them. They're on the top shelf. Four fork handles.... he said what I demanded do you mean by four four candles I'm sure I don't understand well, if you don't, I'm positive I don't he muttered in reply, obviously irritated as he got out his ladder, climbed up it, and fetched from the top shelf — four fork handles what are those I asked what you asked for he yelled and what you've got — Fork Handles!

(20)

(c) Write out the following sentences, putting in the speech marks and any other missing punctuation required, where direct speech is used. Be careful, though, because in some of the sentences reported or indirect speech is also used.

(1) He asked me what I was doing there.

(2) That is very odd in my opinion said the boy.

(3) Dad told him to do it at once without any argument.

(4) Joan said that she had never seen it before in her life.

(5) He answered that is a strange sight.

(6) Come with me he ordered in a voice not to be disobeyed and I will show you sights to dream of not to tell.

(7) Say which one you want then Peter said Ellen.

(8) What do you want I asked but he replied that he wanted nothing save to sit and wait.

(9) Both witnesses claimed that he had said, quite distinctly put up your hands! This is a stick-up.

(10) He opined that it was quite the best he had seen. A first rate example he added warmly.

(30—3 per sentence)

FACTSHEET FIFTEEN

DIRECT AND INDIRECT SPEECH (2)

When you are writing normally, — a composition, story, or letter — you would expect to quote anything said in direct speech. But if you were writing a formal essay or a report, you would use indirect speech.

INDIRECT SPEECH — Reports the exact meaning of what the speaker said.

— Does not report the exact words.

— Does not require inverted commas (as no actual words are involved) or any rule about separate paragraphing.

— Changes pronouns and adjectives in the first and second person (I, you, we, me, us, my, our, your, mine, ours, yours, myself etc.) to THIRD person (he, she, it, they, his, her, hers, its, their, theirs, himself, etc.). The exception is when the main verb is introduced by a first or second person pronoun — I, you, we.

— Changes the tenses of verbs in the speech being reported. Essentially all the action is moved further away. Verbs in the present move into the past (simple past tense or imperfect); verbs already in the past may move even further into the past (so a verb might become pluperfect (the tense formed with '*had*') instead of simply past); verbs in the future tense become conditional, substituting 'should' and 'would' for 'shall' and 'will'.
The tense of the verb in indirect speech depends to some extent on the tense of the verb introducing it, and you will learn more about this in the next Factsheet; for now, try to go by what sounds right.

— Changes anything else that suggests *here* and *now* into *there* and *then*. So *this* becomes *that*, and *these* become *those; today, tomorrow* and *yesterday* become *that day, the following day*, and *the previous day*.

Statements in Indirect Speech are normally introduced by the word THAT.

But be careful: sometimes THAT is missed out altogether, and there is no introductory word.

Questions in *indirect speech* are introduced by the original question word if there was one.

If there was no question word they are introduced by WHETHER or IF.

Commands, originally in the imperative, are done in indirect speech by using the INFINITIVE, *to do* etc.

Look at the following examples which compare *direct* and *indirect speech*:—

DIRECT	INDIRECT
"Are you coming, Tim?" asked Samantha.	Samantha asked Tim if he was coming. ('You' changes to 'he'; tense changes from present to imperfect; question introduced by IF).
"I shall arrive this evening", I said.	I said that I should arrive that evening. ('I' stays the same, because it is 'I' speaking; 'shall' becomes 'should'; 'this' becomes 'that'. We could, incidentally, have put 'would' rather than 'should'.
"Go to my study, boy," said the headmaster.	The headmaster told the boy to go to his study. ('Said' becomes 'told' to introduce the order; 'go' becomes the infinitive 'to go'; 'my' becomes 'his'.)
"What can we do, Jo?" demanded Tina. "If the water rises any more, it will cut us off. — Help!"	Tina asked Jo what they could do. She said that if the water rose any more it would cut them off. Then she cried for help. ('Can' becomes 'could'; 'rises' becomes 'rose'; 'will' becomes 'would'; 'we' and 'us' become 'they' and 'them'. Notice also that we need several speech words to introduce what is said.

Read carefully through the following sentences. They are the basis for the questions in sections (a), (b) and (c) which are set out underneath. You will see that each number consists of a PAIR of sentences.

1. i He said that that was it.
   ii That is it he said.
2. i Open your books children ordered the teacher.
   ii The teacher told the children to open their books.
3. i The announcement came over loud and clear: the flight is cancelled.
   ii The announcement came over loud and clear that the flight was cancelled.
4. i Ben asked Steve what he had put for number three.
   ii Steve, what have you put for number three asked Ben.
5. i I don't know about you Jill said Liz I will be getting out of here as soon as I can.
   ii Liz said that she didn't know about Jill but that she would be getting out of there as soon as she could.

(a) For each question, say for both (i) and (ii) in the pair whether the sentence is in direct or indirect speech. As you can see the speech marks have been left out — it would be rather too easy otherwise!

(10)

(b) One sentence in each pair is in direct speech. Write out each of those sentences again, inserting the speech marks (and any other connected punctuation marks) which have been left out.

(10)

(c) For each pair of sentences, list the differences in the tenses of the verbs, and any other changes and differences you can see, between direct speech and indirect speech.

(10)

(d) Change the following sentences from direct to indirect speech:—
   (1) "It is only me," I said. (QUESTION to think about:— Is this good English, or not?)
   (2) "Are you ready yet, Peter?" Mum asked.
   (3) "Go to your room, Joel," said Dad.
   (4) "I would like," said Ella, "another one of those cakes."
   (5) "Do you want to come with me, Alison?" asked Christopher.
   (6) "Are we going by train or ferry?" inquired Mrs Mackie.
   (7) After giving the order: "Abandon ship!" the captain returned to the bridge.
   (8) "Although things are serious, men," said the captain, "we must not give up hope."
   (9) "If you don't take this map, Marjory, you will get lost," said Bob.
   (10) "Who did you say it is?" he asked.

(20)

(e) Change the following sentences from indirect into direct speech:—
   (1) I ordered Paul to leave the room.
   (2) Cindy asked me if I was coming to the dance.
   (3) I told Cindy that I didn't feel like it.
   (4) He said that he had never seen it before in his life.
   (5) The booking clerk asked me whether I wanted circle or stalls.
   (6) The magistrate asked him why he had done it.
   (7) He replied that it had only been for a bet.
   (8) Lettice announced that she was going to marry Mr Leaf that autumn.
   (9) He claimed that I had said he was a fool.
   (10) I demanded that Mr Rameses return the museum's crocodile immediately.

(20)

FACTSHEET SIXTEEN

SEQUENCE OF TENSES

This topic follows from *indirect speech*, though it applies to other things as well. Look at these examples of indirect speech:-

(1) The boy asked whether he shall go onto exercise two now.
(2) We inquired what they have done.
(3) He asked if he can be excused.

There is clearly something wrong with all three. In each case it is the verb in the piece of reported speech. The tenses used in these verbs (*shall go; have done; can be*) SOUND wrong. If something sounds wrong, more often than not it *is* wrong.

In fact there is a series of rules, known as the SEQUENCE OF TENSES, which covers the correct tenses to use in reported speech. Most of the time you will apply these rules automatically, — and will notice when they are not being applied (as in the above examples). Nevertheless, there are occasions when you will want to check, — particularly if you are trying to put something into reported speech. (If you ever have to write a formal or official report of things that have been said, you will have to do just that!)

The rule of the sequence of tenses, then, is as follows:—

The tense in the piece of reported speech depends on the tense of the verb of saying, speaking, answering etc. that *introduces* the reported speech.

MAIN VERB	VERB following in REPORTED SPEECH
(1) I say (present tense) I am saying (present tense) I do say (present tense) I shall say (future tense) I have said (perfect tense) I shall have said (future perfect tense)	For the present, future, and perfect tenses (and for the rather obscure future perfect), the verb in reported speech can be in ANY TENSE that makes sense. You use the tense closest to that used in the original direct speech.
(2) I was saying (imperfect tense) I said (past tense) I did say (past tense) I had said (pluperfect tense)	For these tenses you must change the verb of the original direct speech, as follows:— SHOULD DO or WOULD DO instead of original SHALL DO WOULD DO instead of original WILL DO MIGHT instead of original MAY COULD instead of original CAN DID instead of original DO WAS DOING instead of original IS DOING HAD DONE instead of original HAS DONE.

Look at these examples, and try to see how this rule works when changing from direct to indirect speech, and vice versa:-

DIRECT:-	INDIRECT:-
"They *will* be coming tomorrow," said Jane	Jane said that they *would* be coming the next day.
"I *shall* remain here,"I replied.	I replied that I *should* (or *would*) remain there.
"Please *may* I go teacher?" he asked.	He asked the teacher if he *might* go.
"How *can* I help you, Tom?" he inquired.	He inquired of Tom how he *could* help him.
"You always *sing* flat, Kate," Mrs Davis had complained.	Mrs Davis had complained that Kate always *sang* flat.
"What *are* you doing with your test tube, Dean?" shouted Mrs Brooks.	Mrs Brooks asked Dean with a shout what he *was* doing with his test tube.
"The committee *has* now reached a decision," were the chairman's words.	The chairman's words were that the committee *had* then reached a decision.
I have repeatedly asked, "*Are* you ready?"	I have repeatedly asked if they *are* ready.
"You *can* come," I tell you.	I tell you that you *can* come.

Notice the last two examples, where the verbs of saying are in the perfect and present tenses, and there is therefore no requirement to make changes to the verbs in the indirect speech. — Just the same, you can still make changes, if you think it improves the sense. (In the last example but one it could have been:— I have repeatedly asked if they *were* ready!)

Also notice all the other changes that have been made between direct and indirect speech.

The sequence of tenses may sometimes also help you decide what tense to use for the verb in other subordinate clauses:—

E.g. We *discussed* his application after he *had left* the room.
   Because she *had* always *tried* hard, she *managed* to pass the exam.
   I *am telling* you this so that you *may* learn something.

Read carefully through the following ten sentences. Some, but not all, of them contain an error in the tense of the verb in the indirect speech. (They all contain indirect speech.) They are the basis for the questions set out in sections (a), (b) and (c) below.

(1)   He asked me what I am doing here.

(2)   Gopal was wondering whether he may go on the trip.

(3)   He said that he will leave on the ten-thirty train.

(4)   She was asking if we have seen her little sister.

(5)   Mr Sanders did not say that we can go.

(6)   I had always thought that sooner or later she would do something disreputable.

(7)   This office has informed you before, Mr Brown, that your application will not be allowed.

(8)   I have complained to the hotel management that my bed was not made yesterday.

(9)   I did not exactly claim that he was a criminal.

(10) The loudspeakers were announcing that the train is finally arriving.

(a)   For each of the sentences above write out (i) the main verb, and (ii) the verb in the piece of reported speech. (There is only one of each in each sentence.) Next to each verb, write down the tense it is in (even if the tense is wrong!)

(10 — ½ each)

(b)   For each sentence, either state 'no mistake' if there is none, or if there is an error, re-write the sentence and correct the mistake in the tense of the verb. (Change the verb in the reported speech, *not* the main verb.)

(10)

(c)   Try to put each of the sentences into direct speech, — making the necessary changes in the tenses of the verbs, the pronouns etc.

(20)

Now read through the next ten sentences, which form the basis for the questions in sections (d), (e), (f) and (g) below.

(1)   "Don't send me to bed yet, Mum," pleaded Janice.

(2)   "I don't want to go to little Cecil's nice birthday party," shouted Billy.

(3)   "Do you want King Edwards, lady?" asked the barrow boy.

(4)   "King Edward can get his own," she replied.

(5)   "A ship of that size could never be sunk," he answered scornfully.

(6)   "Are these two ready to go now?" I had asked yet again at the counter.

(7)   "How dare you defy me, boy?" he shouted.

(8)   Our decision is:— "We will fight, whatever the odds."

(9)   They have called, "Help!" many times today without avail.

(10) I do not ask you: "Is that fair?"

(e)   Say what the tense of the main verb (of 'saying') is in each sentence.

(10)

(f)   Say what tense the verb within the speech marks is in.

(10)

(g)   Put these sentences into indirect speech.

(20)

(h)   Say what tense the verb within the direct speech becomes when you have put the sentence into indirect speech.

(10)

FACTSHEET SEVENTEEN

PUNCTUATION — STOPS & CAPITALS

As you know, a sentence is a group of words which makes complete sense in itself, and does not need any addition to complete it.

You will also know very well that every sentence *must* begin with a capital letter, and end with a full stop, question mark, or exclamation mark.

Full stops are also used after most but not all ABBREVIATIONS. The most common exceptions are 'Mr', 'Mrs', and 'Dr' in front of names — though it is not in fact wrong to put a stop after them. There is a tendency now also to leave out the full stops in very well known abbreviations, like BBC (instead of B.B.C.) and NATO (instead of N.A.T.O.). If you are in doubt, however, it is safest to include the full stop.

Not all abbreviations have capitals; essentially you give an abbreviation a capital letter when the word it is standing for would have had one. You do not of course put capitals for any but the first letter of an abbreviated word:— we write 'Mr', not 'MR'. There are other abbreviations without any capitals:— v. ('versus'), etc. ('etcetera'), cc — or c.c. — ('cubic centimetres').

Some abbreviations gradually turn themselves into real words; these are known as 'acronyms'. 'Radar', now a perfectly acceptable word, began as an abbreviation. 'NASA', (North American Space Agency), still spelt with its capitals, but always pronounced as a word, may be going the same way. There are also strange words like 'SACEUR' (Supreme Allied Commander Europe) to be found.

Most good dictionaries will give you a list of common abbreviations.

Similar to abbreviations are some signs which you may come across:— the ampersand (&) which stands for 'and' (and which you should not really use in your writing, though you will see it quite commonly in books and newspapers); the asterisk (*) which very often marks a reference to a footnote — a little sword-shaped sign is often also used for this as well as small numbers written above the line; you will probably quite often use an insertion mark, ⋋or ∧, yourself, when you have missed out something; — its correct name, incidentally is a 'caret'. The 'oblique' (a slanting line — /) means 'and', or 'or'.

There is one other mark or sign that should be mentioned now, and that is the hyphen. This is a short dash put between two words that are very closely linked together (i.e. though there are two words, they have a single sense). For example:— mother-in-law, passer-by, bye-law, twenty-seven.

The hyphen is also used in words where two vowels occur together but are pronounced separately, such as 'co-operate', and 'no-one'.

Finally, the hyphen is used to indicate the break between two parts of a word when you run out of room at the end of a line, and have to break a word and continue it on the next line. When you do this in your own writing, always split the word in a natural place.

The question mark is a variation on the full stop; its job is (obviously) to indicate a question. Try not to forget it, — but do NOT use it for questions in indirect speech. Look at these two examples:— "Are you coming?" he asked. (Question mark — direct speech); He asked him if he was coming. (No question mark — indirect speech.)

The exclamation mark (!) is also a variation of the full stop. It is used to indicate a word, words or a sentence which is exclaimed or shouted, or just said loudly, or stressed. You are not recommended to use exclamation marks too often; save them for when they are necessary.

One other variant of the stop is the row of dots .... This is used when you leave a sentence unfinished, hanging in the air, or suggesting that there is more to follow but it has been left unsaid. It is often used in stories of suspense and mystery.

Finally there are one or two other uses of capital letters you should be aware of:—

Capitals are required for all proper names, and for proper adjectives formed from them. Little words in proper names, titles etc. are not normally given capitals though (as in 'Burton-on-Trent' and 'A Tale of Two Cities'). 'A' and 'The' as the first word do have capitals. 'God' always has a capital letter, as do words closely linked with 'God' or 'Jesus' (such as 'The Lord' and 'the Word of God') including the pronouns He, Him, His'. 'The Bible' also has a capital.

The first word of a new speaker inside quotation marks always has a capital even when it follows a comma:— 'He asked, "Have you seen James?" "No," I replied, "not since yesterday."

Each new line in poetry must have a capital letter.

And last of all, 'I' standing by itself is always a capital.

(a) Some of the following groups of words could be sentences, some could not. Give the sentences their capital letters and full stops (or exclamation marks or question marks).

(1) without a murmur, although he was very angry, slamming the door behind him

(2) without looking back, an angry look on his face, he left the house

(3) don't do it

(4) stop, thief

(5) after we left

(6) to be or not to be

(7) never put your trust in the promises of a man, my girl

(8) where is my soup

(9) whose name is Fred

(10) despite the lateness of the hour and the difficulties of transportation, a good reason for holding the meeting at very short notice

(11) out with it, then

(12) whatever he may say

(13) and that's not all

(14) over they go

(15) more like a dead duck than a dying swan in my opinion

(16) sweet violets for sale

(17) a dose of salts

(18) which they have arranged to call for us at ten o'clock tomorrow morning

(19) presumably after the collapse of the beer tent and the resulting disturbances

(20) without which, unless an alternative source was found, I suppose   (20)

(b) Using a good dictionary (or any other source of information) find out what the following abbreviations stand for:—

(1) b & b	(7) C.O.	(13) H.R.H.	(19) min.	(25) pp
(2) B.Sc.	(8) Co-op	(14) G.M.T.	(20) m.p.g.	(26) Rev.
(3) Cdr.	(9) D	(15) info.	(21) O.A.U.	(27) s.a.e.
(4) C.I.A.	(10) D.N.A.	(16) kg.	(22) O.E.D.	(28) SF
(5) C.I.D.	(11) E.E.C.	(17) l.b.w.	(23) O.H.M.S.	(29) V.I.P.
(6) cm.	(12) F.R.S.	(18) M.C.C.	(24) P.A.Y.E.	(30) w.p.b.

(15—½ each)

(c) Find out what the following abbreviations of FOREIGN words stand for, and give their meaning in English as well:—

(1) ibid	(3) N.B.	(5) Oxon.	(7) R.S.V.P.	(9) sc.
(2) loc.cit.	(4) op.cit.	(6) pro tem.	(8) R.I.P.	(10) viz.

(5)

(d) Find out what the following ACRONYMS mean:—

(1) ANZAC	(3) GATT	(5) NATO	(7) OPEC	(9) UNICEF
(2) AWOL	(4) NAAFI	(6) RADA	(8) UNESCO	(10) WRNS (pronounced: 'Wrens')

(5)

(e) Write out the following words and phrases, inserting a HYPHEN where one is required:-

(1) front gate	(3) fire engine	(5) long way	(7) bye law	(9) lay by
(2) sky blue	(4) preemptive	(6) thirty eight	(8) wipe out	(10) English book

(5)

(f) Write out the following sentences, giving all the proper nouns (and any other words which should have them) their capital letters:—

(1) He announced the appointment of dr m steel of king's college as regius professor of greek at cambridge university.

(2) In the city of london panic stalked the streets.

(3) The muslims believe in one god, allah, though they recognise jesus christ as a great prophet, second only to the prophet mohammed himself.

(4) They asked me if i wanted to head the corporation, but the presidency was not for me.

(5) Most countries are now republics, which means that they are ruled by elected governments under presidents rather than by kings or queens.   (20)

FACTSHEET EIGHTEEN

PUNCTUATION — COMMAS

A comma indicates a pause rather than a stop. This, incidentally, is something well worth remembering when you are reading. Some people do not pause at all for commas, while others pause too long.

You cannot use a comma as the break between two sentences; this must always be a full stop, question mark or exclamation mark. Still less does a comma act as some sort of join between two sentences. Look at this example:—

'I can see you up that tree, Johnny, you'll have to come down sooner or later.'

The comma after 'Johnny' is wrong. There are two separate sentences here, and we need a full stop. Alternatively, if we wanted to join these sentences we could insert a conjunction (joining word) such as 'but' after the comma.

When you do have a double or multiple sentence with the parts joined by simple conjunctions, do use a comma to indicate the pauses between the separate parts of the sentence, — unless the parts are very short, and to insert a pause is unnecesary. Compare these two examples:—

'She looked all around but she could see no-one.' It would not be wrong to put a comma after 'around', but it is not really necessary.

'She stood anxiously at the gate and looked all around, but before her stretched only a deserted street.' Notice that we can do without a comma after 'gate', but where there is a real pause after 'around' a comma is needed.

Commas are also needed to separate out the clauses and phrases which occur in complex, or simply in complicated, sentences. Once again, they should not be over-done. Simple pieces of description do not need to be separated from what they describe by commas, but long phrases and subordinate clauses normally do need such separation. It makes what you are writing easier to read, and easier to understand. Look at these examples:—

'The man who was responsible claimed in mitigation that he had been under the influence of alcohol throughout the incident.' Now we could put commas on each side of 'who was responsible', and around 'in mitigation', and before 'throughout the incident'. They would not help the sense though, and might make it harder to understand; they would certainly break up the flow if you were reading it.

'After the destruction of the bridge by dynamite, Brigadier White, who had a reputation for quick and decisive action, decided that, despite the serious risks involved, the entire brigade would cross that night by boat.' Here we need quite a few commas to separate the rather long clauses and phrases from each other; without them, it might be hard to make sense of it. Even so, we could perhaps still leave out the commas round 'despite the serious risks involved'.

The rule is:— Use a comma to indicate a pause where it helps the sense; don't use one where it does not.

Commas are also used to separate the individual words in lists (especially long ones). But when you reach the end of a list and the last two words are joined by *and* it is not usual to put a final comma in front of the *and*. Even so, if the last item on the list is a special one that you want to stress, you can still insert the comma if you wish.

The names of people being spoken to, and other words used to address them, are separated from the rest of the sentence by a comma or commas. You also do this with 'yes', 'no', and phrases such as 'thank you'; with adverbs like 'however' and 'nevertheless' used to introduce sentences, and with question phrases tacked onto the end of the sentences (as in:— 'You are coming with us, aren't you?').

By using a pair of commas before and after a word or phrase you effectively separate it from the rest of the sentence.

If you want to separate it more completely, put it in brackets.

You can also use a pair of dashes in the same way. A single dash is used when you are tacking an afterthought or an addition onto the end of a sentence.

The semi-colon (;) is a more forceful version of the comma. You can use it instead of a full stop between two sentences which are closely linked but not joined by a conjunction. (In this case the second sentence will not have a capital letter; a semi-colon, unlike a comma, *can* join two sentences.) You can also use semi-colons to separate items in a list, especially if it is a complicated one, and there are other commas about which might create confusion.

A colon (:) is used to introduce something:— A list, or an example, or a piece of speech. (It is usual to start the item introduced by a colon with a capital letter, and quite commonly the colon is followed by a short dash.)

Finally, the comma (again) is used to separate the thousands in numbers — except dates.

(a)　Correct the punctuation in these sentences. You may have to leave out or add punctuation marks, but you are not to add words or change the order of the words.

   (1)　After we reached the stream. We found the bridge was down.

   (2)　Jack, and Jill went up the hill.

   (3)　Where have you put my shoes, I can't see them anywhere.

   (4)　I don't like cabbage, or parsnips mum.

   (5)　There is nothing I like better, than chips though.

   (6)　I do not know, what I am going to do with you William.

   (7)　We did our homework, then we went out to play.

   (8)　Yes we have no bananas.

   (9)　He opened the door, and went inside.

  (10)　After the ball is over see me take out my glass eye.

(10)

(b)　Punctuate the following, by inserting the missing full stops (including question marks and exclamation marks if there are any), capital letters, and commas:—

   (1)　We will never surrender Herr Töstenfork you will have to fight for every inch of our territory every house and street.

   (2)　You really must get some new clothes Diana and that hat is unbelievable have you no idea of fashion I don't know how you can wear those old things.

   (3)　We were running as fast as we could but there was no chance of escape they had bicycles and they had also sent two of their gang through the backstreets to head us off we were done for!

   (4)　I saw him there governor as clear as anything it was old mr jackson even though he's been dead this past year.

   (5)　Miguel reined in his mule gazing suddenly up towards the outlying mesa above us for a moment he seemed puzzled then he pointed without saying a word and we all saw the glint of steel the briefest flicker amid the long slopes of the Sierra but unmistakable nonetheless.

  (In the five sentences you should have inserted about thirty punctuations marks — including capital letters).

(30)

(c)　Punctuate the following. You will need to insert the following punctuation marks:— comma, semi-colon, colon, dash, brackets.

   (1)　There were 100000 people at the concert not counting those who managed to get in without paying.

   (2)　Never my lad do anything like that again not without telling me first.

   (3)　All those coming on the trip should bring the following heavy boots a change of clothing an anorak and a very great deal of energy.

   (4)　There is not however any good reason and I assure you that I have given careful thought to your objections for further delaying the implementation of the plan

   (5)　Consider carefully the house is very old it needs a damp-course new plumbing and complete re-wiring on the other hand it is in a highly desirable area to sum up my advice to you is to buy it but only if you can negotiate a substantially reduced price.

(20)

FACTSHEET NINETEEN

PUNCTUATION — THE APOSTROPHE

In spoken English we shorten many common combinations of words by squashing out some of the letters and combining the two words into one. This process is shown in written English by using an apostrophe (a comma placed above the line) in the place where the letters have been omitted.

The two most common combinations of words are those between PRONOUN AND VERB, and those between VERB AND NEGATIVE.

The personal pronouns (I, you, he, she, it, we, they) combine with the auxiliary verbs and the various forms of the verb to be to produce the following:—

He'd (He had or he would or he should); he'll (he will); he's (he is or he has)

I'll (I will or shall); I'd (I would or should or had); I'm (I am); I've (I have)

It's (It is or it has:— notice that this is the ONLY time you spell *it's* with an apostrophe)

She'd (She had or would or should); she'll (she will); she's (she is or has)

They'd (They would or should or had); they'll (they will); they're (they are:— notice this as well, and try not to confuse it with 'there' and 'their'); they've (they have).

We'd (we would or should or had); we'll (we shall or will); we're (we are); we've (we have)

You'd (You would or should or had); you'll (you will); you're (you are); you've (you have).

Similarly from combinations of these verbs with 'that', 'there', 'who' etc. we get such forms as:—

That's (that is or has); there'd (there would, should or had); there's (there is or has); who'd (who had or would or should); who'll (who will); who's (who is or who has: do not confuse it with 'whose' which means 'belonging to whom'); who've (who have).

You can do much the same with nouns:— 'Tom'll do it'; 'Jack's the lad'; 'The milkman's been.'

Here is a list of the abbreviations formed by combinations of verbs with NOT:—

aren't; can't (in full this is written 'cannot'); couldn't; didn't; doesn't; don't; hadn't; hasn't; haven't; isn't; mustn't; shan't (in full 'shall not'); shouldn't; won't (in full 'will not'); wouldn't.

There are a few other abbreviations of this sort in common use. *O'clock* (short for 'of the clock') is probably the most common. *E'er* (ever) and *e'en* (even) are poetic (and there are various other poetic forms). *'Twas* (it was) and *'Tis* ('it is') are old-fashioned (though children still shout *'Tis!* — *'Tisn't* at each other). *Ain't* (meaning 'am not, are not, is not, has not, have not'!) is not supposed to be good English, though it once was.

After all that, in your own writing it is best not to use many of these abbreviations with apostrophes. Some people regard them as rather poor English. You can of course use them as much as you like in direct speech within quotation marks, though.

The other use of the apostrophe is to indicate POSSESSION.

Possession is shown in THE SINGULAR, by putting an APOSTROPHE FOLLOWED BY THE LETTER 'S' after the word standing for the person or thing which is the possessor.

So, *The girl's book* means *the book of the girl,* or *the book belonging to the girl.*
The Queen's palaces means *the palaces that belong to the Queen.*

(Put the 'aspostrophe S' on the owner, not on the thing owned.)

BUT most words in the plural in English already end in S. So they have a different rule:—

Possession is shown FOR PLURAL WORDS ENDING IN -S by putting an APOSTROPHE AFTER THE 'S' (which is already there).

So, *The girls' mother* means *the mother of the girls.*
The soldiers' boots means *the boots of the soldiers.*

DO NOT FORM PLURALS BY USING THE APOSTROPHE. Things like:— 'There are four boy's in our class', 'Cabbages' for sale!' are just gibberish.

Finally, there are some plurals in English that do not end in -S (like 'men, women, children, geese, cannon, mice').

FOR PLURAL WORDS THAT DO NOT END IN -S, show possession by adding APOSTROPHE 'S' — as if they were singular.

So, *The children's toys* meaning *toys of the children.*

NOTE:— Singular words ending in 'S' form the possessive by adding another apostrophe 'S'.

But *names* ending in -S may add apostrophe 'S', or simply an apostrophe — *Jones's or Jones'.*

(a) Write out the following sentences, inserting an APOSTROPHE wherever one has been missed out:—

(1) Whos been eating my porridge?

(2) Whats up, Doc?

(3) Ive never seen anything like it in my life.

(4) She said shed come as soon as she was ready.

(5) You cant do it; I dont want to hear any arguments; and thats final.

(6) Thatll do! I wont have that sort of language in my kitchen!

(7) Theyll come down here at once if they know whats good for them.

(8) Its three oclock already, so youd better hurry up, hadnt you?

(9) Theyre the only ones weve got at the moment.

(10) The milkmans been but he obviously hasnt read your note as theres one pint here.

(20)

(b) Now write out the sentences again, this time putting in the FULL FORMS of the words abbreviated with apostrophes.

(20)

(c) In each of these sentences there is a mistake involving words that should or should not be spelt with apostrophes. Re-write the sentences correcting the mistakes.

(1) Look out! There coming!

(2) That poor horse has broken it's leg, I think.

(3) Who's book is this, and why hasn't it been put away?

(4) Are these mine, your's or mother's?

(5) Do you have any new potato's, or haven't they come in yet?

(6) Well, wi'll you come, or won't you?

(7) I can'not make head or tail of number seven.

(8) They'res a unicorn on our front lawn, dear, and it's eating the roses.

(9) Its going to rain again, so you'd better bring your umbrella.

(10) Lets have a go; it looks pretty simple to me.

(10)

(d) Use apostrophes to form the possessive equivalents of the following. (For example:— one book of more than one girl = The girls' book.)

(1) one song of one bird

(2) more than one song of more than one bird

(3) one lid of one box

(4) one lid of more than one box

(5) one toy of one baby

(6) more than one toy of more than one baby

(7) more than one crash of more than one vehicle

(8) one crash of more than one vehicle

(9) one mother of one child

(10) more than one mother of more than one child

(11) one dress of one lady

(12) one dress of more than one lady

(13) more than one dress of one lady

(14) more than one dress of more than one lady

(15) more than one goose of more than one man

(30)

(e) Correct the errors in the following sentences connected with the use of the apostrophe:—

(1) The ladys had beautiful hats.

(2) The ladies hats' were beautiful.

(3) The ladies dress' were expensive.

(4) She has twin baby boys'.

(5) There were lines of lorries along the roads to the docks

(6) I bought ten pounds of potatoes'.

(7) The price of ten pounds' of potatoes amazed me.

(8) The childrens' voice's filled the corridors.

(9) Ours is the people's party.

(10) He had hundreds of deers' antlers mounted on his walls.

(10)

FACTSHEET TWENTY

PUNCTUATION — SPEECH

As you already know, direct speech *must* be placed inside quotation marks (also known as speech marks or inverted commas).

But do try to remember that indirect speech must not be given quotation marks. Direct speech states the exact words that were actually spoken. Indirect speech reports the same sense but it does not use the actual words spoken, and therefore does not have quotation marks.

In indirect speech the word of saying or speaking is normally linked to the speech by a connecting word, very often 'that'.

In direct speech there is no 'link-word'. A comma is placed between the word of saying or speaking and the words spoken (unless there is another stronger punctuation mark there — i.e. a question mark or exclamation mark). The comma marking this separation should be put INSIDE the quotation marks — unless the word of saying or speaking comes before the piece of speech. It is not as complicated as it sounds; look at these examples:—

She asked, "Where on earth have you been all day, Luke?" (The comma after 'asked' is outside the quotation marks; the question mark is inside.)

"I've only been down the recreation ground," he answered, "playing with Benedict." (The comma after 'recreation ground' and the final full stop are inside the quotation marks, but the comma after 'he answered' is outside.)

When you have a sentence as in the second example above, with the words of saying/speaking inserted in the middle of the speech, remember to ensure that the quotation marks exclude them. Also notice that when the speech resumes it does not need a second capital letter as it is not a new sentence. A capital letter is needed when the *beginning* of the speech follows an introductory word as in the first of the examples above.

Whenever there is a new speaker, or a change of speaker in a piece of dialogue in direct speech, their words should be given a new paragraph. Look at this small piece of dialogue set out correctly:—

"Why," mother asked, "are you wearing those swimming trunks over your jeans, Adam?" She waited for a while, and finally he answered:—

"They're part of my costume."

"What do you mean, costume?" asked his father. "You're just wearing ordinary clothes."

"I haven't put the towel on yet," said Adam. "Then I'll be Superman."

Notice how to make the paragraphing work when you have the speaking/saying word before the piece of speech it is introducing; a colon (and dash) is employed instead of just a comma.

The other use of the paragraph — the indenting of words from the margin at the beginning of a piece of writing — is to mark off different sections in the passage. You should try to divide up all your writing into paragraphs, so that it comes in reasonably sized chunks for the reader.

You will have noticed by now that there are two forms of quotation marks; one using double inverted commas ('sixty-six and ninety-nine'), the other using single inverted commas. Both are in fact equally correct in all cases. However, it is quite sensible to make a distinction, and in your writing to use the double-commas form for all piece of genuine direct speech, and to use the single-commas form for any other requirements. There are other uses for quotation marks. They can be used to state (or 'to quote') examples, as they are normally used in this book. They can also be put round words used in a special way (particularly 'ironically' or as a sort of joke; or words, that should be stressed or emphasized in reading). You should also put quotation marks around 'quotations'; these are pieces of (other people's) writing which you include in your own writing. This is true also of any titles of books etc. which you may mention, as in the following examples:—

'But cricket is different', as Mr Mallalieu so rightly remarks in 'Test Match Gallery'.

"I cannot abide 'Pickwick Papers'," I remarked, "or 'A Christmas Carol', or any of the works of Dickens."

In printed material italics (slanted writing) can be used for titles, or for showing words that should be given special stress or emphasis. In your writing you will need to use quotation marks, though you can, alternatively, just underline titles or words you want to stress.

There is one last kind of punctuation mark you may come across:— the accent. Accents — à (grave), é (acute), ô (circumflex) — are found above vowels in some foreign words. It is also the custom to put foreign words you use in italics (or quotation marks). You may also come across the umlaut (ü), the tilde (ñ), the cedilla (ç), and some even stranger forms. You may also meet the diaeresis — two dots placed over a letter to show it is pronounced separately (ä).

(a) Insert the missing punctuation in the following pieces. In addition to speech marks, some capital letters, full stops, commas, exclamation marks and question marks will be required; some of the punctuation is already there to 'help' you.....

(1) What he asked do you want

(2) After that he said with an angry glance you won't have to sack me. You can have my resignation

(3) He said that it wasn't him, and continued to protest that he was innocent all day. You know me he told us. Would I do a thing like that never

(4) That is what I said he insisted and that is what I meant.

(5) I have always said that that was the case, and my advice to you is that you should say exactly the same as I do.

(6) Wait for me, and I'll come were his words. He told me to wait for him, so I waited. Wait he said — so I waited, but what he had promised was never to be.

(7) She said I am grown weary now. She gave a sigh and said I know my time has come.

(8) I heard him as clearly as I hear you, sir said the butler earnestly. Pour me a glass of brandy, Gumboyle, was what he said. Old Gumboyle paused. Then he took down a volume of Decline and Fall of the Roman Empire, and told me that I could go, he added.

(9) If in fact my client did admit that he was responsible — and I must insist that he said no such thing — then I can only state that he did so as a result of unwarrantable pressure from those officers who were questioning him.

(10) I told him that I had not said Give me a gin, but Time to begin and he said I don't believe a word of it, and brought me a gin.

(You should have inserted a total of about SIXTY pieces of punctuation in the ten questions).

(30)

(b) Punctuate the following completely. ALL punctuation has been missed out. The approximate number of pieces of punctuation required for each is given you at the end.

(1) im not standing for all these changes he said they arent right in fact theyre downright wrong (14)

(2) in the napoleonic wars the safety of britains commerce of the channel and of the english coast depended on the efforts of the royal navy alone (12)

(3) rob roy though many regard it as highly entertaining i remarked is not my favourite among the works of scott (14)

(4) oh we dont want to lose you but we think you ought to go (5)

(5) there can be no question of his having been present at the scene of the crime on the night in question (2)

(6) king charles I walked and talked half an hour after his head was cut off (6)

(7) for sale grand piano in solid mahogany only one owner elderly lady with carved bow legs and claw feet (6)

(8) whos there demanded lucy its me shouted edward at the top of his voice dont you mean it is i said lucy no its not you silly its me came the answer with a giggle (41!)

(NB — Remember in number eight to start new paragraphs for new speakers; that counts as a piece of punctuation.)

(50—½ each)

TESTSHEET ONE

Factsheets 1 to 6

(a) For each of these sentences, write out (i) the SUBJECT and (ii) the FINITE VERB. Remember that both may consist of several words, and that they may be split up.

   (1) The author of so many mysteries had now herself become part of one.

   (2) Bradley, the boy with the spelling problem, has finally begun to take extra English lessons.

   (3) To have tolerated this state of affairs any longer would have been quite impossible for all concerned.

   (4) Making difficulties and getting in the way has, in my opinion, always been your primary role in life.

   (5) Without a major cash injection from the shareholders, financing a project of this complex nature could not possibly be contemplated by the directors of this bank.   (20)

(b) Write out the following sentences and insert the correct form of the verb from the two choices given you in the brackets.

   (1) The jury (consist/consists) of five men and seven women.

   (2) Neither James nor Jonathan (have/has) handed in (his/their) book.

   (3) A long line of cars (are/is) blocking the road.

   (4) Stuart and Douglas (is/are) coming on the trip.

   (5) Our most distinguished admiral and the victor of Trafalgar (is/are) dead.

   (6) Each of them (is/are) equally responsible since both (have/has) been warned of the possible dangers involved.

   (7) The gipsy encampment, with all its brightly painted caravans, and horses, and lines of clothes, and bare-foot children (presents/present) a gaudy sight to us drab and conformist city-dwellers.

   (8) A herd of deer (was/were) grazing in the meadow.   (20)

(c) Use the following verbs in sentences of your own; firstly TRANSITIVELY and secondly INTRANSITIVELY. (So you will write two sentences for each verb; make it clear which is which).

   (1) act   (2) sing   (3) fly   (4) read   (5) try   (20)

(d) In the following sentences say whether the words underlined are parts of transitive or intransitive verbs:—

   (1) He was <u>sitting</u> quietly reading a book.   (4) He was <u>falling</u> down a long, sloping shaft.

   (2) I will <u>sink</u> this putt if it's the last thing I do.   (5) What have you <u>done</u> with your life, Melissa?

   (3) <u>Give</u> me another scotch and soda, steward.   (10)

(e) In the following sentences say whether the words underlined are parts of a FINITE verb or a NON-FINITE verb:—

   (1) He was, after all, only <u>minding</u> his own business.   (4) <u>Put</u> the whole lot on 'Bookie's Darling' to win.

   (2) <u>Making</u> clay pots somehow doesn't appeal to me.   (5) The <u>elected</u> member refused to make a statement.

   (3) You could not wish to <u>see</u> a better performance.   (10)

(f) For these questions, write out every example of the following parts of the sentence you can find:— OBJECT; INDIRECT OBJECT; COMPLEMENT. You may find that some sentences may contain more than one of these, — and some none of them. Label each one carefully, — and if there is none in a particular sentence, say so.

   (1) There will be trouble about this.

   (2) No, I have honestly not said a word to her, Josephine.

   (3) Why on earth did you give that awful man such a good reference?

   (4) It seemed only a moment since our last meeting.

   (5) I prefer to stay in and read.

   (6) We saw before us the vast expanse of the limitless ocean stretching out forever into a blue infinity beyond the far horizon.

   (7) Suddenly, the whole building, no the whole city, was collapsing in ruins about me.

   (8) So why was he writing himself letters?

   (9) The surface of the curious substance felt smooth to the touch.

   (10) We waited, and we wondered, but we were never to know.

          (20)

Factsheets 7 to 13

(a) Classify the following as:— simple; double; multiple; or complex sentences; — or as not a sentence.

(1) I have never heard such a ridiculous story.

(2) A story to which no-one could give any credence.

(3) They were all idealists, and they believed in liberty, equality and fraternity.

(4) He asked me what I was doing.

(5) I looked out, saw that it was raining, and went back inside.   (5)

(b) The following sentences may be simple, double, multiple or complex. Divide each of them into its MAIN clause (or more than one main clause), and SUBORDINATE clauses (if there are any). Clearly label each clause as 'main' or 'subordinate'.

(1) I could not hear what he was saying.

(2) After listening to the news I went to bed feeling tired and unhappy.

(3) When I heard the news, although it was not unexpected, the shock which it gave me left me quite helpless for a moment.

(4) I wondered where she had got to, but put the thought out of my head, and made a cup of coffee.

(5) There can be no agreement until the French, who are being typically obstructive, admit that Britain's position is both logical and compelling.

(6) I poured my tea, stirred it absent-mindedly, and then put the sugar in.

(7) With a long sigh, still weary after the previous day's alarms and excursions, I looked up curiously at my unexpected and somewhat unwelcome visitor.   (20)

(c) For each of the following sentences:—

(i) Write out each subordinate clause or phrase;

(ii) Identify it as *clause* or *phrase*;

(iii) State whether it is *noun, adjective* or *adverb clause/phrase*;

(iv) If it is a noun clause/phrase, state whether it is subject, object or complement;
If it is an adjective clause/phrase, state which word it is qualifying/describing;
If it is an adverb clause/phrase, state which type it is.

(1) I have never seen a marrow of such impressive dimensions.

(2) Reading a good book is my favourite occupation.

(3) The boy you want is hiding under the bed. (TWO)

(4) Show me what you are doing.

(5) If they do not come soon, we shall go without them. (TWO)

(6) Despite the rising waters, we did not panic.

(7) When he had gone, I opened the envelope.

(8) The person whose book it is should claim it immediately.   (40)

(d) Analyse the following simple sentences. The categories in your analysis should be:—
subject (divided into *subject word* and *extensions*), and predicate, with the predicate divided into *verb, extensions of the verb,* and *completion of the verb* (the last consisting of:— *object, indirect object, complement,* which in turn have their main or key word plus their extensions). Obviously not all sentences contain all categories.

(1) The sound of the stream filled the little glen with merriment.

(2) I have already been discussing the matter in hand with Mr Davis.

(3) With an angry cry he sprang to his feet.

(4) Send me a copy of the letter.

(5) That particular material has always seemed adequate in the past.   (15)

(e) Analyse the following complex sentences. In addition to the categories mentioned in the instructions for (d), you will also need to add the categories:— *clause; clause type; connection.*

(1) When you have finished that report, there is a letter I would like you to type.

(2) I looked in the butcher's window as I went past, but all the meat was far too dear.

(3) If that is the time, I fear that I shall be late.

(4) Though she did her training as a scientist, she has made her career in politics.

(5) The girl who apparently wrote the best essay has not been awarded the prize because we discovered that she had copied most of it from an English textbook.   (20)

43

Factsheets 14 to 20

(a) Put the following into indirect speech:—
    (1) "I have never seen you before," she answered.
    (2) "Come here at once, Jonathan," shouted his mother.
    (3) "What do you want with me?" Sarah asked.
    (4) "If I go this way, I shall be sure to get lost," muttered Bob.
    (5) "You said, 'That's my bucket'," he insisted pedantically.
    (6) "What are you doing here, White?" asked Brookman.
    (7) "Watch it, Brookman," answered White, "or there'll be trouble."
    (8) "Did you see that? — Look up there!" he shouted.
    (9) "Cherries for sale! Lovely ripe cherries!" came the market trader's voice.
    (10) "The train now approaching platform thirteen is the 15.30 for Salisbury," crackled the announcer's voice over the loudspeaker. "Stand well clear of the platform edge." (20)

(b) Put the following into direct speech:—
    (1) I said that you would be coming.
    (2) I told Mr Lambert that you had come.
    (3) We asked David to show us his painting.
    (4) It was reported in 'The Telegraph' that Derek Sawyer would now be opening the batting for England in the Fourth Test.
    (5) I advised Hugh not to write his memoirs.
    (6) The barrister insisted his client was innocent.
    (7) Kevin asked Paul if he wanted a fight.
    (8) Paul replied that he didn't mind at all if Kevin didn't.
    (9) I answered that I had never promised that I would do it.
    (10) We claimed our rights. (20)

(c) Insert the missing *capital letters, full stops, exclamation* and *question marks* in the following:—
    (1) he asked me if i had read tennyson's 'lady of shallot' my answer was, "no"
    (2) we will soon have to elect a new principal, following mr sanders' appointment as chairman of the governors of the bbc
    (3) "do you want this," asked ella, "or shall we throw it away"
    (4) her majesty the queen arrived in washington dc yesterday, where she was met by the president
    (5) he stopped and looked back then he began to run towards park lane, where he turned again the kgb man was still there (20)

(d) Insert the missing *commas, semi-colons, colons,* and *dashes* in the following:—
    (1) these are the instructions turn left opposite the post office just past Woolworth's that is after about a hundred yards or so take a right and then a sharp left cross over the zebra crossing and the entrance is on your right the one with the red door.
    (2) After hearing this not relishing my extraordinary mission and also being filled with a general apprehension I made the necessary arrangements with Wilkinson my trusted servant packed a travelling bag made the reservations and left for New Delhi immediately.
    (3) I am not sure if it is so my boy if it is then I am quite amazed and a little shocked. (10)

(e) Insert the missing *apostrophes* in the following:—
    (1) Ive got the childrens presents here.
    (2) You mustnt do that to the nice ladys hat, Billy.
    (3) Wheres Mandys pudding, Tom?
    (4) Ben says he definitely hasnt seen those soldiers machine gun.
    (5) What do you mean, 'Shes cutting off the mices tails'? (10)

(f) Insert the missing punctuation in the following sentences. The main things you will have to put in are *speech marks;* but there are various other marks needed, particularly *commas.*
    (1) If you don't come with me, you'll regret it I told him.
    (2) What I asked are we supposed to do with a container-load of mangoes
    (3) I do not think was his reply that you should do that.
    (4) I explained what action I would feel bound to take if he was caught, but all he said was Go ahead! I couldn't care less. (20)

Revision Test

(a) For each of these sentences write out (i) the subject, and (ii) the verb. Remember that some verbs involve more than one word; also, you will find that some of the subjects are quite long!

(1) The light of dawn at last began to paint its colours on the landscape of night.

(2) What on earth are we all to do now?

(3) To return once more to the land of my birth will forever remain my dearest wish.

(4) Sitting by the fireside, engrossed in the latest novel of his favourite author, James was not at all disposed to get up and answer the door.

(5) Without some hard evidence, no-one, however committed to one or other side in this debate, would want to come to a firm conclusion either way.   (10)

(b) Put in the right form of the verb from the choices in brackets:—

(1) A row of trees (marks/mark) the line of the road.

(2) What (were/was) Sheila and I to do now?

(3) The admiral, with over six hundred men, (has/have) been drowned in the wreck.

(4) A large shoal of herring (were/was) said to be in the vicinity.

(5) Not only the church wardens, but also the rector, (is/are) objecting.   (10)

(c) Classify the following sentences as SIMPLE, DOUBLE, MULTIPLE or COMPLEX. Divide them up into their constituent MAIN and/or SUBORDINATE CLAUSES and next to each clause write whether it is main or subordinate.

(1) He asked me what I had seen.

(2) Without a thought for herself she offered her own life in place of his.

(3) While you're away I'll always think of you, and write to you every day.

(4) Janet saw her, gave a shout, and waved her umbrella in the air.

(5) The government have decided to force through this measure in the face of a united opposition, but its passage through parliament is bound to be a stormy one.   (15)

(d) Analyse the following sentences as fully as you can. (Some of them are complex sentences.)

(1) I tell you that there is no smoke without fire.

(2) Where has great-grandmother put her spectacles?

(3) Give me a good English breakfast, and I'll be fit for the rest of the day.

(4) When the blaze reached the peak of the great bonfire the Guy caught alight with a roar and crackle of flames.

(5) If the management of this firm do not organize their affairs in a more efficient manner, I for one do not see how the workforce on the factory floor can ever achieve the stipulated production targets.   (20)

(e) (i) Change the following sentences from direct to indirect speech:—

(1) "Are you coming to the pictures tonight, Joe?" asked Mary.

(2) "I'd rather make it tomorrow," he answered, "if that's alright with you."

(3) "Pass me that fly swatter would you, Peter," said Dad.

(ii) Change the following sentences from indirect to direct speech:—

(4) She asked Alice if she knew who would be coming to her (Alice's) party.

(5) He claimed that he was innocent, and insisted that he had never seen that man before that night.   (10)

(f) Punctuate the following passage. It is quite complicated, and you may need to add as many as seventy punctuation marks (including capital letters, paragraphs etc.)

after he had finished his performance i saw him leave the stage and then without changing out of his costume disappear via the fire exit of course i hurried after him in the street there was noone to be seen not at first that is then my eyes happened to light on a stray scrap of paper not of course what i had been looking for at all which proved to contain a very curious message ill quote it in full go to east street the one by woolwich docks there you will find a mr a smith at no thirtyseven take with you a rope a knife £1000 in cash and a heavy duty sack and do not under any circumstances forget this note you can imagine my amazement at such a singular message which was signed capt c ponsonby fo   (35)

Revision Test

(a) For each of the following sentences write out (i) the finite verb (which may of course consist of more than one word), and (ii) the object, indirect object or complement. If the sentence has none of these write 'no object/ complement'. Bear in mind that a sentence can have more than one object, and can certainly have both an object and an indirect object.

    (1) We have all, from time to time, been angry with ourselves.

    (2) Who has sent Miss Chandler these lovely flowers?

    (3) French is taught to the older pupils by the Headmaster.

    (4) With a final effort I threw the distant form bobbing helplessly in the sea the heavy water-sodden line.

    (5) Mr Dawes would certainly appear by far the best candidate for the post. (10)

(b) Change these sentences in *all* respects from the singular to the plural. (The words you generally have to change are the nouns, pronouns and verbs.)

    (1) I was watching the criminal's house.

    (2) Never trust a pretty woman, lad.

    (3) He'll never know now if it's true or not.

    (4) Will you write me a letter when you get there?

    (5) Has she sent the lady's dress to the shop? (10)

(c) In each of the following sentences there is one subordinate clause or phrase.

    (i) Write out the clause or phrase.

    (ii) Say which it is, clause or phrase.

    (iii) Say whether it is *noun, adjective* or *adverb* clause/phrase.

    (iv) If it is a noun clause/phrase, say whether it is subject or object of the sentence;
        If it is an adjective clause/phrase, say which word it is qualifying or describing;
        If it is an adverb clause/phrase, classify it according to the different types.

    (1) I asked her what she was doing there.

    (2) She was a girl with bleached-white hair and the palest complexion.

    (3) Though he may be a criminal, he is still my husband.

    (4) With a last despairing effort, he reached the ledge above.

    (5) To write a good novel is my ambition. (20)

(d) Write the following in the simple possessive form. (I.e. *one toy of one boy = the boy's toy.*)

    (1) more than one banana of more than one child

    (2) one tail of one cat

    (3) more than one dress of one lady

    (4) the thatch of more than one roof

    (5) more than one cannon of more than one army (10)

(e) Insert the apostrophes which have been missed out in the following:—

    (1) Hed said he wouldnt want one of ours.

    (2) Its yours Jack, so dont miss it.

    (3) Whos afraid of the big bad wolf?

    (4) If thats really what hes up to, Im absolutely amazed.

    (5) Were now certain she didnt do it. (10)

(e) Analyse the following sentences. (Some of them are complex sentences.)

    (1) The War Office have finally sent Captain Courtney's mother his effects.

    (2) After Jackson had given him the package, he looked furtively around, and then hailed a taxi.

    (3) The object, which we now saw clearly for the first time, was metallic and completely spherical.

    (4) Exactly what do you think you are doing in there?

    (5) The aged clerk, who had not even noticed my arrival, was writing methodically, with a pen that squealed in protest as he dragged it across the paper, in a ledger more vast and compendious than any I had ever seen before. (20)

(f) Punctuate the following passage:—

give me a stiff one jacko i ordered and downed the drink in one i looked quizzically at him do you know a guy called ponsonby in answer to my question he merely shrugged hes something to do with dr mendra the illusionist playing the old alhambra in surrey street i added and as he obviously needed sweetening pushed a ten pound note across the bar you dont want to get mixed up in that mr slade he answered this bloke you want well hes dead the old bill have already been sniffing round here about him and some other geezer too that said he was from the foreign office in whitehall (20)

INDEX AND SUMMARY